1974

University of St. Francis
GEN 575.12 S962
Sutton
Genes, enzymes, and inherited

Y0-BRH-227

GENES, ENZYMES, AND
INHERITED DISEASES

LIBRARY
College of St. Francis
JOLIET, ILL.

These Studies are designed to inform the mature student—the undergraduate upperclassman and the beginning graduate student—of the outstanding advances made in various areas of modern biology. The books will not be treatises but rather will briefly summarize significant information in a given field and interpret it in terms of our current knowledge of the rapidly expanding research findings within the life sciences. Also it is hoped that the Studies will be of interest to teachers and research workers.

BIOLOGY ⟵
STUDIES

H. Eldon Sutton
The University of Texas
Austin

GENES, ENZYMES, AND
INHERITED DISEASES

Holt, Rinehart
and Winston
New York • *Chicago* •
San Francisco •
Toronto • *London*

DECEMBER, 1966

COPYRIGHT © 1961 BY HOLT, RINEHART AND WINSTON, INC.
LIBRARY OF CONGRESS CATALOG CARD NUMBER: 61-7862
ALL RIGHTS RESERVED

28233-0111
PRINTED IN THE UNITED STATES OF AMERICA

5 75. 12
8962

preface ►►►►►►

It was only 60 years ago that the principles of genetics were rediscovered. Few of the contemporary sciences can claim so recent a beginning. After a long period of adolescence during which the more formal aspects were the major object of study, genetics is now reaching a mature phase, in which it has attracted the efforts of experimentalists from many disciplines—for example, physical chemistry—that are useful in the study of gene structure and action. At the same time, the medical profession has found it necessary to give greater attention to the genetic component of those diseases, metabolic and degenerative, that occupy an increasing proportion of medical care. Thus the boundaries between genetics—or geneticists—and related disciplines are becoming much less distinct.

The purpose of this monograph is to review some of the recent findings on the chemical nature of genes and gene action and to relate these findings to the production of inherited diseases. With so complex a subject, it has been necessary to assume on the part of the reader some familiarity with basic genetics, biochemistry, and physiology. It is hoped that this will not discourage those readers whose backgrounds in these areas are minimal. Any attempt to synthesize the various aspects of biochemical genetics and inherited disease was felt to be incompatible with an oversimplified treatment.

In preparing this manuscript for publication, the author would like to acknowledge his debt to colleagues in the Department of Human Genetics, the University of Michigan, who have discussed many aspects of these topics with him. Particularly he would like to recognize Drs. James V. Neel, Margery W. Shaw, Charles R.

67550

Shaw, and Richard E. Tashian, who read parts or all of the manuscript and made many helpful suggestions regarding the presentation of material. If many pitfalls have been avoided, the credit must be shared with them.

H. E. S.

Austin, Texas
April, 1961

contents

chapter one ► Introduction

Just as classical genetics had to be rediscovered before it became accepted, so biochemical genetics also was discovered, ignored, and then rediscovered. The first clear statement of the biochemical expression of inherited variability was by A. E. Garrod, who summarized some of his thoughts in the Croonian lectures of 1908. Garrod was remarkable in the insight he had into several aspects of genetic problems, and he clearly set forth the concept of a metabolic block in alkaptonuria.

The very aspects of the contemporary scientific climate that made Garrod's insight so remarkable also caused his work to be overlooked. This was a time when Mendelian genetics was not completely accepted, certainly not as the general explanation of heritable variation. Furthermore, Garrod's observations were made on human material—patients with rare diseases—where controlled experimentation was impossible. And the discipline of biochemistry was still in its infancy, being primarily concerned with the qualitative nature of biological materials.

With the elucidation of the major features of formal genetics attention again turned in the 1930s to the chemical mechanisms of gene action. By this time biochemistry had also reached a somewhat more sophisticated level. With the work of Beadle and Tatum it became apparent that genetic variation could be associated with discrete metabolic events and that gene action could be described in biochemical terms. This has led to considerable understanding of the chemical nature of genes and their functional mechanisms.

The existence of biochemical genetics implies the existence of

1

nonbiochemical genetics, and indeed the practitioners of genetics tend to classify inherited traits into a variety of arbitrary categories —biochemical, morphological, immunological, etc. It should be clearly understood that these distinctions are only operational. Genetic variation can be expressed in a variety of ways, and a scientist groups together those traits that fall under his particular observations. This should not be interpreted as implying a closer relationship among the anthropometric traits than between anthropometric and biochemical. Indeed, the action of a single gene may be detected by both anthropometric and biochemical techniques.

If genes are classified on the basis of their primary action, there is no alternative to considering all gene action as chemical. It is difficult to imagine any plausible mechanism of gene action that is not mediated by chemical reactions and forces. While the lack of man's imagination is not a compelling argument in science, the modicum of cases that have been adequately analyzed conforms completely to this theory. For this reason the study of biochemical genetics is considered the key to understanding the nature of genes and their role in cell function.

As an illustration of the central nature of the primary biochemical effect of genes, we may consider the sequence of events arising from the inherited defect in hemoglobin structure known as sickle cell hemoglobin. A person homozygous for sickle cell hemoglobin has sickle cell disease. In this disease the red blood cells assume bizarre shapes in the absence of adequate oxygen (Fig. 1-1). The consequences of these abnormal erythrocytes are varied, as shown in Fig. 1-2. The myriad effects observed in sickle

Fig. 1-1. The sickling of erythrocytes (A) in individuals heterozygous for the sickle cell gene, and (B) in individuals homozygous for the sickle cell gene. (From Neel and Schull, 1954, p. 171.)

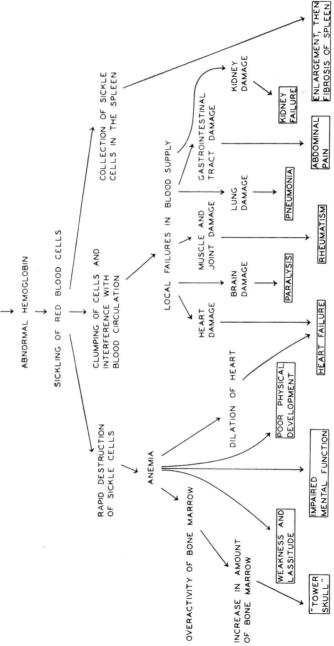

Fig. 1-2. A pedigree of causes for sickle cell anemia. The single defect in hemoglobin structure is responsible ultimately for the great variety of manifestations of this disease. (From Neel and Schull, 1954, p. 172.)

3

cell disease can logically be traced to a single chemical change. Such "pedigrees of causes" have been constructed for a number of inherited diseases, always with some single variation in chemical activity or structure as the primary defect.

Man has often been looked upon as a collection of organs. To be sure, it is often the failure of a specific organ that causes difficulty for its owner. Such thinking, however, has given rise to false concepts of heredity. We speak of inheriting a certain type of nose or ear or perhaps an eye defect. True, the principal visible manifestation of what is inherited may be in these structures; but, as the iceberg shows only a part of itself above the water, so an inheritance shows only a part of itself in a type of nose or ear or eye defect. It is increasingly realized that virtually all genes exert their influence throughout the body. As tissues differentiate their responses to various gene products may undergo marked quantitative changes. One tissue may rely heavily on a particular reaction to supply energy. An inherited defect in that energy supply will affect that tissue more than it will affect another tissue that uses a different source of energy. While it is still frequently useful to describe the consequences of gene action in terms of organ effects, this must be done with the realization that every cell in the body carries the same defective genes and that analysis of gene action at the chemical level may give quite a different picture from a description based on morphological considerations.

A fundamental aspect of genetics that must be appreciated is that study is limited to inherited *variation*. The inheritance of hair color cannot be studied in a population in which everyone has black hair. Morphological traits involve the function of many genes, but the individual genes can be identified only if they exist in at least two modifications. If only one gene is present in modified form, then the morphological trait will often be said to be under the control of one gene. This statement is not literally correct; it is the variation that is under the control of a single gene.

From the foregoing it can be seen that it is unrealistic to separate chemical traits from other manifestations of gene action. Since we are concerned primarily with the nature of genes and the mechanism of gene action rather than with the expression of specific genetic systems, however, it is convenient to limit our attention to those manifestations that can be described in chemical terms. Part

of the inconvenience of discussing genetic and environmental interaction in differentiation and development arises from the paucity
of knowledge of the mechanisms involved. Here and there we have
glimpses of these mechanisms, but for the most part our knowledge
is descriptive.

This monograph is not intended to be a comprehensive survey
of inherited diseases or of human genetics in general. It will deal
instead with the principles that are important to all genetic
processes. For information on specific diseases the reader is referred
to some of the monographs listed below.

GENERAL REFERENCES

Human Genetics, General

NEEL, J. V., and SCHULL, W. J., 1954. *Human Heredity*, Chicago: The University of Chicago Press. 361 pages.
PENROSE, L. S., 1959. *Outline of Human Genetics*, New York: John Wiley.
ROBERTS, J. A. F., 1959. *An Introduction to Medical Genetics*, London: Oxford University Press. 263 pages.
STERN, C., 1960. *Principles of Human Genetics*, 2d ed., San Francisco: W. H. Freeman. 753 pages.

Molecular Genetics

ANFINSEN, C. B., 1959. *The Molecular Basis of Evolution*, New York: John Wiley and Sons. 228 pages.
Exchange of Genetic Material: Mechanisms and Consequences, Cold Spring Harbor Symposia on Quantitative Biology 23, 1958.
Genetic Mechanisms: Structure and Function, Cold Spring Harbor Symposia on Quantitative Biology 21, 1956.
DE GROUCHY, J., 1958. *L'hérédité moléculaire. Conditions Normales et Pathologiques*. Rome: Istituto Gregorio Mendel. 333 pages.
MCELROY, W. D., and GLASS, B. (eds.), 1957. *The Chemical Basis of Heredity*, Baltimore: Johns Hopkins Press. 848 pages.
PONTECORVO, G., 1958. *Trends in Genetic Analysis*, New York: Columbia University Press. 145 pages.
STRAUSS, B. S., 1960. *An Outline of Chemical Genetics*, Philadelphia: W. B. Saunders. 188 pages.
SUTTON, H. E. (ed.), 1960. *First Conference on Genetics*, New York: Josiah Macy, Jr. Foundation. 229 pages.
WAGNER, R. P., and MITCHELL, H. K., 1955. *Genetics and Metabolism*, New York: John Wiley and Sons. 444 pages.

Inherited Metabolic Diseases of Man

HARRIS, H., 1959. *Human Biochemical Genetics,* Cambridge: Cambridge University Press. 310 pages.

HSIA, D. Y.-Y., 1959. *Inborn Errors of Metabolism,* Chicago: The Year Book Publishers. 358 pages.

SORSBY, A. (ed.), 1953. *Clinical Genetics,* London: Butterworth. 580 pages.

STANBURY, J. B., WYNGAARDEN, J. B., and FREDERICKSON, D. S., 1960. *The Metabolic Basis of Inherited Diseases,* New York: McGraw-Hill. 1477 pages.

LITERATURE CITED

GARROD, A. E., 1908. "Inborn errors of metabolism," *Lancet* ii, 1–7.

chapter two The Molecular

Structure of Genes

THE CHROMOSOMAL THEORY OF INHERITANCE

Of the cell processes that can be observed with a light microscope, surely one of the most interesting and intricate is cell division—especially the replication and distribution of chromosomes into daughter cells. These elongated, deeply staining bodies appear in the nucleus prior to cell division. The number, size, and individual morphology are essentially constant for all the members of a given sex and species. After each chromosome has split longitudinally to form two identical daughter chromatids, all the chromosomes align themselves in a plane through the center of the cell. This is followed by separation of the chromatids, the two members of each pair migrating to opposite ends of the cell. The cell then divides to form two daughter cells, each with an exact replica of the chromosome complement of the parental cell.

The above description is a very simplified version of somatic cell division, but it serves to emphasize the precision with which chromosomes are distributed during mitosis. Virtually the only other biological traits known to be under comparable control are inherited variations. This suggested to the early geneticists that chromosomes might in fact be the physical structures that carry genetic information. The theory was verified when it proved possible to associate specific aberrations in chromosomal structure with specific inherited traits.

7

If we are ultimately to understand the chemical basis of inheritance, we must start by studying the chemical structure of chromosomes. Although some success has been attained in isolation and direct chemical assay of chromosomes, most of the results have been obtained by cytochemical methods. These include the use of ultraviolet microspectrophotometry, which is based on the fact that nucleic acids absorb very strongly at 260 mμ; the Feulgen stain, which is specific for deoxyribonucleic acid (DNA) and which can be quantified; and digestion with specific enzymes, such as ribonuclease. Some of the results obtained with these early techniques have recently been confirmed by the use of tritiated thymidine, in which part of the hydrogen is replaced by the radioactive hydrogen isotope tritium. Thymidine is incorporated only into DNA; and labeled thymidine, detected by exposure of photographic film, can therefore be used to reveal the presence of DNA.

The various approaches to the chemical composition of chromosomes agree that DNA is a substance unique to chromosomes. Furthermore, although there is considerable variation among species, the amount of DNA per nucleus is essentially constant within a species. Exceptions to this rule are found in gametes, which have half the usual amount of DNA (and half the normal somatic complement of chromosomes); special tissues in which giant chromosomes are formed; and tissues such as liver, in which cells with double the normal complement of chromosomes frequently occur.

Basic proteins—the histones and protamines—are found in close association with DNA. There appears to be some variation in the amount and kind of basic protein present in different types of cells. The experimental techniques available for the study of basic proteins leave unsatisfactorily answered a number of questions concerning the significance of these unusual compounds.

A third constituent of chromosomes, present only in small amounts, is ribonucleic acid (RNA). Unlike DNA, it is distributed throughout the cell. It is present in high concentrations in the nucleus, particularly in the structure known as the nucleolus. The microsomes in the cytoplasm are also RNA-containing structures.

Finally, chromosomes contain a greater or lesser amount of nonbasic protein, depending on the tissue in question.

Examples of the amounts of these substances found in chromosomes are given below, in Table 1. In addition to these large molecular weight substances, there are also small molecules present

Table 1

The Composition of Chromosomes Based on Typical Results
Obtained from the Analysis of Mass-isolated Material
The relative values of these constituents will vary widely depending on
the tissue used for isolation. (From Thorell, 1955.)

Substance	Amount, in percent
DNA	40
RNA	1
Basic protein (histones)	50
High molecular weight protein	8

in the chromosome. It seems unlikely that these would act as a repository of genetic information. They may have an important function in maintaining the structural integrity of chromosomes, however. Calcium, in particular, is thought to play such a role.

EVIDENCE FOR DNA AS THE CARRIER OF GENETIC INFORMATION

Early attempts to determine which of the above substances might actually constitute genes—or, in the preferred terminology of today, might be the actual carrier of genetic information—were hampered by lack of knowledge concerning the structure of nucleic acids. Nucleic acids were known to be large polymers, but whether they could exist in the array of structures necessary to specify the many functions that are genetically controlled was uncertain. Proteins, on the other hand, by the permutations and combinations of amino acids, were known to have the potential for storing vast amounts of information.

At this point we may consider some of the attributes of a substance that might serve in a genetic capacity. The first requirement is that the substance must exist in many different forms. This is obvious from the fact that every organism contains thousands of genes, each distinguishable from the others. Each distinguishable species must differ from other species by a minimum of one gene, and the total number of different genes that exist or have existed must be larger than the total number of species that have existed. Simpson (1952) has roughly estimated that the total number of species that have existed is 500 million. Thus, 500 million plus

20,000 would be a conservative estimate of the number of distinguishable genes ever in existence. The molecules that comprise genes must be capable of existing in at least as many forms.

A second requirement for a suitable genetic material is that it be stable, both with regard to external physical agents and to metabolic action. Mutations do occur in genetic material, but they are relatively rare (ca. 1×10^{-5} per functional locus per gamete). A third requirement is the ability to direct the production of an identical copy. It is obvious that genes replicate somehow and that they do so with great accuracy. Besides this *autocatalytic* function, genes also have a *heterocatalytic* function. That is, they direct the synthesis of the numerous enzymes that carry out cellular activities and give rise to what we observe at the phenotypic level.

Table 2
DNA Content of Various Cells, in Grams $\times 10^{-12}$ per cell. (From Vendrely, 1955; Leuchtenberger, *et al.*, 1954.)

Organism	Kidney	Liver	Erythrocytes	Sperm
Chicken	2.4	2.5	2.5	1.3
Cow	6.4	6.4	—	3.3
Carp	—	3.0	3.3	1.6
Man	5.6	5.6+[a]	—	2.5

[a] In addition to the usual diploid cells, liver has many tetraploid cells. This causes the mean DNA per cell to be higher than the diploid amount. If individual cells are studied (Leuchtenberger, *et al.*, 1954) the DNA content corresponds either to the diploid amount or to a multiple of the diploid amount.

Although conclusive evidence was not forthcoming until the work on pneumococcal transformations, two other approaches first suggested that DNA might be the key substance of heredity. The first was the observation that the induction of mutations by ultraviolet irradiation was most efficient at 260 mμ (Hollaender and Emmens, 1941). It has already been mentioned that nucleic acids are characterized by their strong absorption at this wavelength. It seemed possible, therefore, that the mutations were being induced through the absorption of energy by nucleic acid. Both types of nucleic acid absorb at this wavelength, but DNA is quantitatively more important in chromosomes. An objection to this reasoning is that DNA may in fact absorb the energy but pass it on to some more critical molecule that by itself is incapable of absorbing at this wavelength.

A second observation was that the amount of DNA, in contrast to other substances measured, is constant from cell to cell within a given species—with the major exception of gametes, which have half the normal complement of chromosomes and half the normal amount of DNA (Vendrely, 1955). This is illustrated in Table 2 above. Again this suggested that DNA might play an integral role in gene action. The role could be that of a supporting structural element, however, rather than that of the primary genetic material. The lack of constancy of other substances may merely reflect the lack of discrimination of the analytical methods.

Transformation

The best evidence for DNA as the genetic material appeared in 1944, in a classic paper by Avery, MacLeod, and McCarty. Their studies were based on some observations of Griffith reported in 1928. Pneumococci are small, somewhat elongated bacteria usually encased in a thick capsule of polysaccharide. When plated on solid media they form smooth, shiny colonies. Occasionally a mutant arises which forms a rough, dull colony on solid media. The latter are found to have lost the ability to synthesize the polysaccharide capsule. It is possible to recover smooth forms from rough by appropriate methods of selection. A number of different types of pneumococcus are recognized on the basis of immunological differences in the capsule type. These differences are genetically controlled, and mutation from one type to another has never been observed. When a rough form reverts to a smooth form, it always reverts to the original type from which it was derived.

Griffith observed that, if he simultaneously injected into a mouse a living culture of rough cells derived from one capsular type along with a heat-killed culture of smooth cells of another capsular type, he could eventually recover from the mouse living smooth cells of the second capsular type. The rough cells injected alone never yielded smooth cells of the second type. These findings are indicated diagrammatically in Fig. 2-1. Various combinations of capsular types were tested, and the phenomenon was found to be a general one. Subsequent investigators were able to effect the same transformation *in vitro* by mixing living cells and extracts from killed cells of different capsular types and selecting for growing cells of the killed type.

Avery, MacLeod, and McCarty (1944) isolated the transforming

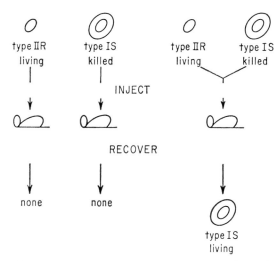

Fig. 2-1. The transformation of pneumococcal capsule types by simultaneous injection of living and killed cultures into mice. (Based on studies of Griffith, 1928.)

principle and reported its chemical and physical properties. They concluded that the active substance was DNA because (1) analysis of elements gave results to be expected for DNA, (2) chemical tests revealed the presence of DNA but of no other substance, (3) no immunologically active substances could be detected, (4) only DNase destroyed the transforming activity, and (5) the substance behaved as if highly polymerized, as DNA is. Subsequent studies with more highly purified material and crystalline enzymes have verified that it is indeed DNA that possesses the transforming activity. For example, Hotchkiss (1952) has prepared pneumococcal transforming principle that has less than 0.02 percent protein. In addition to the studies with pneumococci, transformations have been successfully carried out in several other microorganisms and with a variety of genetic markers.

Bacteriophage infection

Another indication of the importance of DNA in transmitting genetic information is found in the studies of bacteriophage infection reported by Hershey and Chase (1952). These bacterial viruses consist entirely of protein and DNA. By the use of S^{35} to label proteins and P^{32} to label DNA, it had been shown that the DNA is completely encased within a protein envelope. A diagram of the anatomy of a phage particle is shown in Fig. 2-2. The ability to adsorb onto a sensitive bacterium is a property of the antigenic

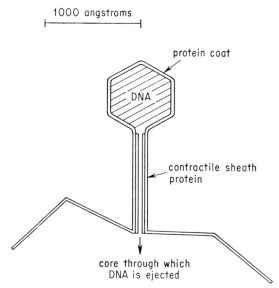

1000 angstroms

protein coat

DNA

contractile sheath protein

core through which DNA is ejected

Fig. 2-2. Diagram of a bacteriophage particle. Except for the core of DNA, the entire structure is composed of protein. The point of attachment to the bacterium is at the bottom. When the contractile sheath contracts, the point of the "tail" penetrates the bacterial wall and DNA is extruded into the cell.

structure of the protein coat and not of the DNA. Each strain of bacteriophage has its specific range of host cells to which it can attach.

Hershey and Chase found that by applying a strong shearing force (Waring blender) to a mixture of sensitive cells and phage particles shortly after the particles had become attached to the host cell, they could knock off the adsorbed phage particles and recover them separately from the bacterial host cells. Analysis of the radioactive sulfur and phosphorus indicated, however, that, although most of the protein was recovered, most of the DNA was still in the host cell fraction. In fact, removal of the empty protein coats did not influence the course of development of new phage particles within the host.

Investigations using radioactive tracers as outlined above have demonstrated that, soon after a phage particle adsorbs onto a sensitive bacterium, it injects its DNA core into the bacterium. At this point the empty protein coat has completed its function. The injected material has all the information necessary to direct the production of new phage particles, including both DNA and protein portions, within the host cell. Careful studies of the composition of the injected material indicate that it is 97 percent DNA and 3 percent protein. There is little reason to doubt that it is the DNA that carries genetic information into the host.

RNA as a carrier of genetic information

Although DNA appears to be the ultimate repository of genetic information for nearly all species of plants and animals, there is one class of organisms that depends on RNA for storage of information—the RNA viruses, which include plant viruses and some animal viruses (for example, influenza and poliovirus). Purified preparations of these viruses are devoid of DNA, yet they are fully infective and capable of producing new virus particles. The RNA virus that has been studied most extensively for genetic function is tobacco mosaic virus (TMV). Electron microscopy and x-ray diffraction studies have shown TMV to consist of a hollow spiral of protein units, with RNA sandwiched between successive turns of the spiral near the hollow core.

It has been clearly demonstrated that the RNA is responsible for transmitting inherited characters. Fraenkel-Conrat and his associates (1957) were able to separate RNA from the protein portion and then to recombine them into infective particles. Indeed, it was possible to combine the RNA from one strain of virus with the protein part from a related but distinguishable strain and still get infective particles. The infection resulting from these hybrid particles was always the same as the strain from which the RNA had been extracted. Some of these results are shown in Table 3.

Gierer and Schramm (1956) were able to demonstrate the function of RNA in tobacco mosaic virus even more clearly when they developed a method for isolating RNA that retained its infectivity in the absence of protein. Such RNA preparations, when inoculated into tobacco plants, produce lesions characteristic of the

Table 3

Results of Recombination Experiments in Tobacco Mosaic Virus

The two strains of TMV and HR can be distinguished by the types of lesions that they produce. (From Fraenkel-Conrat, *et al.*, 1957.)

Strain supplying		Disease symptoms
Nucleic acid	Protein	
TMV	TMV	TMV
HR	HR	HR
TMV	HR	TMV
HR	TMV	HR

intact virus and yield virus particles complete with their proper protein.

Since both DNA and RNA can function in the transmission of genetic information, the question is raised whether DNA and RNA are truly alternatives to each other, or whether the two nucleic acids function in a cyclical manner in all organisms. If the latter is true, it is possible that DNA controls the synthesis of RNA, which in turn synthesizes more DNA. In the case of the RNA viruses, it would be the RNA phase that is incorporated into the inert particulate phase. In other organisms it would be the DNA that is in the inert or gametic phase. The evidence at present is inconclusive. As later discussions of DNA replication will indicate, however, it seems probable that the first hypothesis must be correct. Even though DNA and RNA may both carry genetic information, their functions in the cell are not necessarily analogous.

THE STRUCTURE OF NUCLEIC ACIDS

Since nucleic acids can function in a genetic capacity, it is of interest to inquire into their structure to ascertain what structural elements serve as the integral part of the genetic code. Considerable success has been achieved in formulating a structure for DNA to meet most of the requirements of the experimental evidence.

Nucleic acids are high molecular weight polymers composed of subunits called nucleotides. Each nucleotide consists of a purine or pyrimidine base, a five-carbon sugar, and a phosphate group. One nucleotide of RNA (adenylic acid) has the structure shown in Fig. 2-3. Other RNA nucleotides differ only in the purine or

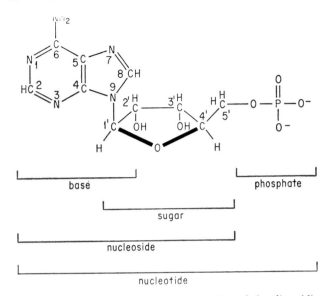

Fig. 2-3. Structure of adenosine-5'-phosphate (adenylic acid).

pyrimidine base that is present. The adenine of adenylic acid can be replaced by guanine, cytosine, or uracil.

The nucleotides of DNA are similar to those of RNA except that the sugar is D-2-deoxyribose rather than D-ribose. The bases found in DNA are adenine, guanine, cytosine, thymine, 5-methyl-cytosine, and 5-hydroxy-methyl cytosine. A summary of the composition of nucleic acids is given in Table 4, below. The structures of the bases found in nucleic acids are given in Fig. 2-4.

In the polymerized form in which they are found in nucleic acids, nucleotides are connected to one another by formation of an ester bond between the phosphate group of one nucleotide and the 3'-hydroxyl of the adjacent nucleotide. Thus, long chains can be built up in which the backbone consists of alternating sugar and phosphate groups with purine and pyrimidine bases projecting from the sugar groups.

These basic facts about the constituents of nucleic acids and the positions of the connecting bonds have been well established. They constitute, however, only part of the picture of nucleic acid structure—the primary structure. DNA isolated in the native state forms viscous solutions in which many of the functional groups

Table 4

The Constituents of RNA and DNA

		DNA	RNA
Bases:		adenine	adenine
		guanine	guanine
		cytosine	cytosine
		thymine	*uracil*
		5-methylcytosine[a]	
		5-hydroxymethylcytosine[b]	
Sugars:		D-2-deoxyribose	D-ribose
		D-glucose[c]	
Acid:		Phosphoric	Phosphoric

[a] Replaces part of cytosine in some species.
[b] Replaces cytosine entirely in some bacterial viruses.
[c] Conjugated with 5-hydroxymethylcytosine in those bacterial viruses that contain the latter.

appear to be tied up so that they are not available for titration. Heating denatures DNA, thereby reducing the viscosity and releasing the functional groups so that they can be titrated, but without

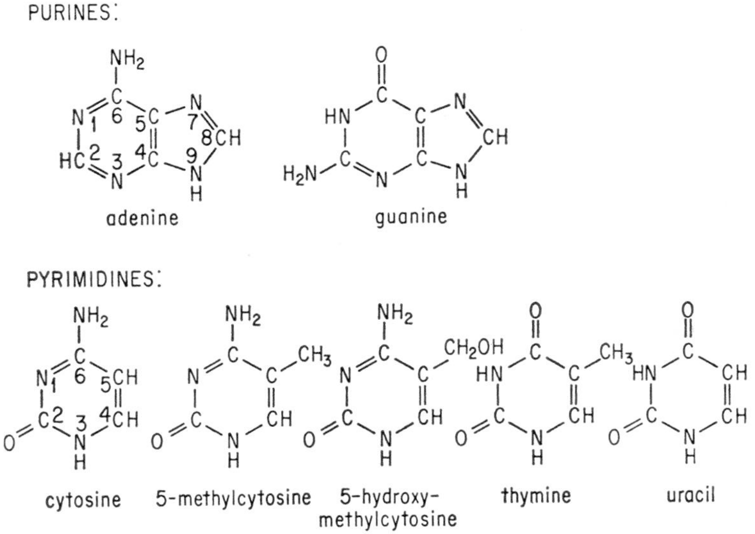

Fig. 2-4. Structures of bases that occur in nucleic acids.

destroying covalent bonds. The existence of structural relationships involving forces other than the simple covalent bonds raises interesting questions. Which of the structural features is responsible for the biological activity—the sequence of bases projecting from the sugar-phosphate backbone, or some more complex steric or spatial feature? Or can the two aspects be separated?

The secondary structure of DNA

The availability of good crystalline preparations of DNA has permitted detailed studies of secondary structure. X-ray diffraction studies of DNA crystals indicate that the polynucleotide chains are arranged in a helical form in the crystal and that each helix consists of more than one chain. The titration studies mentioned above suggest that the amino groups of the bases are connected by hydrogen bonds to other atoms in the molecule. The formation of hydrogen bonds imposes certain geometrical restrictions on the location of the participating groups.

Analyses of various DNA preparations for the relative frequency of the four principal bases suggest that certain restrictions may exist in the occurrence of these bases (Chargaff, 1955). For example, the ratio of adenine to thymine does not deviate significantly from 1.0. Likewise, the ratio of guanine to cytosine is approximately 1.0. The ratio of adenine (or thymine) to guanine (or cytosine), however, may vary widely. Examples have been found from 0.4 to 1.9. Thus adenine and thymine nucleotides may somehow be associated with each other in DNA, as may guanine and cytosine nucleotides.

With essentially this knowledge and rather detailed information on bond distances and angles of nucleotides, Watson and Crick (1953a) were able to construct a model that conformed quite well to the known requirements for a DNA molecule. They postulated that two polynucleotide chains are arranged parallel to each other so that the bases of one chain match the bases of the other chain. In order to maintain the chains the same distance apart, it is necessary to match a purine in one chain with a pyrimidine in the other. Finally, in order to hold the two chains together, it is necessary to form hydrogen bonds between the paired purines and pyrimidines. The only pairing that would keep the chains uniformly separated is adenine with thymine and guanine with cytosine (Fig. 2-5). If such a model is constructed, it is found that the deoxyribose-phosphate chain is not quite perpendicular to the plane of the

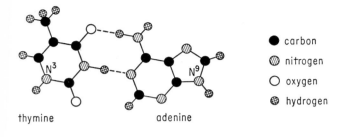

thymine   adenine

● carbon

◍ nitrogen

○ oxygen

⊕ hydrogen

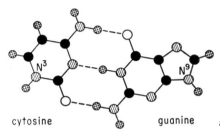

cytosine   guanine

Fig. 2-5. The pairing of DNA nucleotide bases. Dotted lines indicate hydrogen bonds. The distances between pyrimidine N^3 and purine N^9 are very similar in the two pairs.

bases; hence, with each succeeding pair of bases the whole structure will rotate slightly (36 degrees). The result is a right-hand helix with 10 base pairs per complete turn. A portion of a DNA molecule is illustrated in Fig. 2-6.

The validity of the structure proposed by Watson and Crick is generally acknowledged. Particularly in its favor is the fact that it can be used to predict accurately the x-ray diffraction data that is experimentally obtained (Wilkins, 1956). No other model yet proposed can do this.

The Watson-Crick model has certain features that recommend it as the primary carrier of genetic information. First, a tremendous number of configurations is possible, even with a fairly small piece of DNA, because any of four nucleotides may be at each nucleotide position. For example, for n positions the number of configurations is 4^n. For $n = 10$—one complete turn of the helix—the number of configurations is 1,048,576. Fifteen nucleotide positions would provide more than the 500 million estimated as the minimum number of genes that have ever existed. These calculations are unrealistic, since they ignore the possibility that some nucleotide positions may not function as part of the genetic code. Furthermore, as will be discussed later, many configurations are probably nonsense. Never-

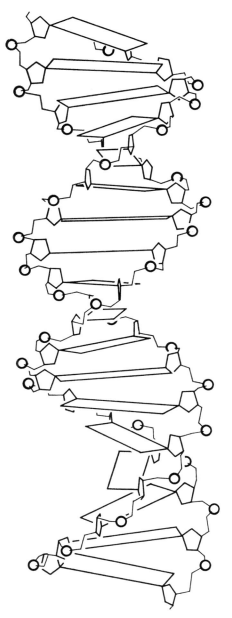

Fig. 2-6. Diagram of a portion of a DNA molecule according to the model of Watson and Crick (1953a).

theless, they illustrate the efficiency with which DNA can store information.

Another feature of the Watson-Crick structure of interest to geneticists is the dual nature of the helix. Since a base on one polynucleotide chain can be paired only with a specific base on the other—for example, adenine with thymine—the two chains are in effect complementary copies of each other. Thus, if a sequence of nucleotides is specified for one chain, then the sequence on the other chain is automatically specified, even though it is a different sequence from the first. The term "nucleotide position" as used in the preceding paragraph is therefore equivalent to two nucleotides—one on each chain. It is common to speak of a "base pair" or "nucleotide pair" as the variable unit when discussing problems of coding and storage of information.

Since the two strands of the DNA double helix are related reciprocally, each strand should be capable of directing the formation of the other. In other words, if the strands were separated, each should be able to serve as a template for the synthesis of its complementary strand (Watson and Crick, 1953b). The result would be two identical double helices instead of the original one, each of which would contain one strand from the original and one newly synthesized strand. Thus we see that the Watson-Crick structure provides a model for the replication of genetic material. This will be further explored in a later section.

Studies of DNA from a variety of natural sources indicate that the double-strand helix is by far the predominant form. For example, it is possible to obtain x-ray diffraction patterns from intact sperm heads clearly showing the double helix scattering (Wilkins, 1956). A significant exception has recently been reported by Sinsheimer (1959). This exception occurs in bacteriophage ϕX174, one of the smallest of the viruses. The total DNA in a single virus has a molecular weight of only 2 million, compared to molecular weights for DNA from other sources of greater, possibly much greater, than 10 million. Physical and chemical studies of the DNA isolated from this phage are consistent with a single-strand structure. The pattern typical of the double helix is missing from the x-ray diffraction pattern, titration curves indicate that the amino groups are free rather than tied up in hydrogen bonds, and the base ratios do not conform to the usual value of 1.0 for adenine to thymine and for guanine to cytosine.

The existence of a stable single-strand DNA that is biologically active raises the question of whether DNA passes through a single-strand stage in other organisms. It is also a matter of speculation whether the DNA of ϕX174 goes through a double-strand stage during replication in the host cell. It has been suggested, for example, that the double-strand form of DNA is an inactive form and that the active form is the unwound single-strand form. The experimental evidence is inadequate to decide among these possibilities.

Relevant to the question of the relationship of DNA to gene and chromosome structure is the molecular weight of DNA. The usual method of estimating molecular weights of giant polymers is based on sedimentation rate in an ultracentrifuge. Earlier studies of DNA suggested that the molecular weight is about 6 million. This would correspond to approximately 9000 nucleotide pairs with a total length of 3 microns. More recently, higher sedimentation values have given molecular weights up to 12 million.

These values may be grossly in error. A study of Davison (1959) showed that rather a large amount of fragmentation of DNA molecules occurs as a consequence of mechanical agitation during preparation of the sample and insertion into the centrifuge. By exercising extreme care Davison was able to obtain much higher sedimentation values on DNA from bacteriophage than is obtained by the usual techniques. These higher values would correspond to a molecular weight of 100 million, if calculated by the relationship between sedimentation and molecular weight that holds at much lower sedimentation values. Thus most of the DNA in a phage particle appears to constitute a single molecule. Considerable error may be introduced in this extrapolation. Even if it is 100 percent, the size of the DNA molecule would be very much larger than previously thought.

It has been demonstrated that linked genetic traits can be introduced together into a bacterium by the process of transformation (p. 11). Whether the transforming particles are single molecules (or fragments of the original molecule), or whether they are aggregates of molecules, is not known. It seems probable that more than one trait can be carried on a single DNA molecule. If this is the case one may ask, as Levinthal has, what evidence is available to show that the DNA in a chromosome consists of more than one molecule (Levinthal, 1960). In man the amount of DNA per haploid complement is 2.5×10^{-12} grams (Table 2, p. 10). This would correspond to 1.5×10^{12} atomic weight units. The average molecular weight per chromosome would be $(1.5 \times 10^{12})/23 = 6.5 \times 10^{10}$. The smallest chromosome in man comprises only 1.25 percent of the total haploid chromosome length (Chu and Giles, 1959). Considering this to represent a proportionate amount of DNA, the molecular weight of this chromosome would be 2×10^{10}. This would be equivalent to 200 molecules of molecular weight 1×10^8 or to about 28 million nucleotide pairs. The length of this DNA would be 10^8 A, or 1 centimeter. The actual length of the chromosome is only about 1.5μ during metaphase. This discrepancy requires that the DNA molecules be folded or coiled in order to conform to the dimensions they occupy in cells.

There are too many assumptions involved in the above calculations for them to be taken literally. With the recognition that measurement of sedimentation of DNA is a much more difficult problem than previously thought, it will be necessary to restudy DNA from a variety of sources. There is no reason at present to assume that the molecular weight of phage DNA is similar to that of mammalian DNA. The mammalian DNA could be smaller, or it could be very much larger. As the length of DNA increases, the problems of replication are not made easier. Nevertheless, it would be premature to exclude the possibility that each chromosome indeed contains very few molecules and perhaps only one of DNA.

The structure of RNA

It is much more difficult to obtain crystals of RNA than of DNA, and x-ray diffraction studies have not indicated the regularity of secondary structure that characterizes DNA. On the basis of titration studies and viscosity measurements, RNA is thought to be a single polynucleotide strand without a consistent secondary structure. Regularities in base composition such as those typical of DNA do not seem to occur in RNA.

For RNA it should also be possible to place any of the four bases in any nucleotide position. As in the case of DNA, this would permit storage of information. Certainly in the RNA viruses and in some steps of protein synthesis, this must be the case. To what extent the storage of information in RNA is analogous to storage in DNA has yet to be ascertained. The recent demonstration that RNA and single-strand DNA from the same source can associate into a double-strand structure supports the idea that the base sequences of RNA are specific and related to those of DNA (Hall and Spiegelman, 1961).

THE FINE STRUCTURE OF GENES

The internal structure of genes can be approached by two routes, chemical and genetic. In the previous section the chemical nature of genetic material was discussed, with suggestions as to the mechanism by which information is stored. The genetic approach is also informative and, as we shall see, complements the chemical studies remarkably well.

One of Mendel's original discoveries was the independent assortment of inherited traits, that is, the principle that the probability that two different traits will be transmitted by a parent to a given offspring is the product of the separate probabilities that each trait will be transmitted to the offspring. When the chromosomal theory of inheritance came into being it was realized that independent transmission should occur only if the two traits are on different chromosomes. This theory was verified experimentally. For example, in *Drosophila melanogaster,* which has four pairs of chromosomes, the great number of known genes can be grouped into four linkage groups, the genes within a group being transmitted as a unit while the groups themselves are transmitted independently.

A most useful exception to this rule occurs as a result of the phenomenon of crossing over. In higher organisms when a diploid cell in germinal tissue begins meiotic division, which will eventually result in haploid gametes, the homologous chromosomes pair so that a locus on one chromosome is opposite the corresponding locus of the other chromosome. By a process still not understood the paired chromosomes are able to exchange segments. The result, shown in Fig. 2-7, is a reassortment of linked genes. Although only one crossover is shown in Fig. 2-7, it is possible to have two, three or more in a chromosome pair. The farther apart two genes are situated on a chromosome, the more likely it is that a crossover will occur between them. Conversely, two genes that rarely reassort at meiosis must be very close together. By measuring the frequency with which recombination occurs among a series of genes it is possible to construct a linkage "map" in which the genes are arrayed on a linear scale. The distance between marker genes is expressed as the percent recombinants found among the progeny of

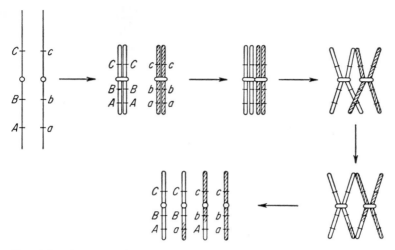

Fig. 2-7. A pair of homologous chromosomes undergoing synapsis and crossing-over during meiosis. The interchanged segments have produced two new combinations of genes, giving a total of four different haploid cells (gametes).

a parent carrying the genes. If the genes are not linked at all (on different chromosomes), then the recombination value should be 50 percent. If genes are sufficiently distant on the same chromosome, then crossing over may occur at least half the time, in which case a value of 50 percent will also be obtained. It is therefore necessary to add up a series of smaller distances to establish linkage between two genes that are located on the same chromosome more than 50 recombination units (or centimorgans) apart.

A process analogous to crossing over exists among many microorganisms even though the regular meiotic pattern of higher organisms is lacking. In bacteriophage and some bacteria homologous sections of DNA are presumed to align themselves during replication of DNA so that the newly forming DNA occasionally switches from one parental template to the other. If the parental templates differ by at least two genes, and if a switch-over occurs between these two genes, the result is a newly formed piece of DNA in which recombination has occurred. This process is illustrated in Fig. 2-8. Since there has been no physical interchange of segments, the term "crossing over" is not appropriate and the more general term "recombination" is usually employed. Crossing over yields two

LIBRARY
College of St. Francis
JOLIET, ILL.

67550

reciprocal recombinants; this "copy-choice" mechanism yields a single recombinant. The probability of a switch-over between any two genetic markers is a function of the distance by which they are separated. Hence, one-dimensional recombination maps can be constructed similar to those based on crossing over.

parental DNA
strands

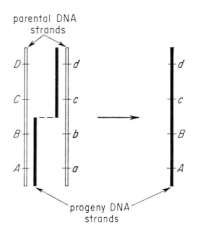

Fig. 2-8. Recombination of genetic markers by means of a copy-choice mechanism in certain lower organisms. In this diagram, the daughter DNA has switched from one parental strand to another between markers B and C. The result is a single piece of progeny DNA with two markers from each parent.

progeny DNA
strands

Thus far in the discussion, the word "gene" has been used without a specific definition, only as a *unit* of heredity. At this point we must consider some of the operations by which a gene is defined. Perhaps the most common concept of a gene is as a portion of the chromosome responsible for a single function. It is necessary again to emphasize that genetically we recognize genes only if variation exists at some specific locus on the chromosome. Furthermore, the inherited variations that we observe usually represent lack of function by the locus as compared to the normal function that produces a "wild-type" organism. From the altered function of the variant individual, a normally functioning unit in other individuals can be inferred. It is therefore possible to define a gene as a unit of function. This definition should picture a gene as the smallest unit capable of directing independently of other loci a single function. The word "directing" is used rather than "carrying out," since actual performance may be very much dependent on other loci.

Genes can also be defined in terms of their ability to mutate, since they are recognized only through the existence of variant forms. A gene may therefore be considered the smallest segment of a chromosome capable of undergoing change and thereby causing a change in function.

A third means of defining a gene is based on recombination, which is discussed above. Experimentally the scientist usually deals with genes that are physically separated on the chromosome. Under such circumstances, when crossing over occurs between two genes it nearly always occurs far enough away from either gene so that the nature of the gene boundary is of little consequence. Recombination does occur between very closely linked genes, and earlier workers considered that it should be possible to define the boundaries of genes as the points at which crossing over can occur. Thus we have as a third definition of a gene the smallest unit of the chromosome capable of recombining with other units.

These three definitions were based on the concept of a gene as a bead on a string, with each bead carrying out some unit function. A mutation involved changing the nature of the bead, and recombination involved crossing over between the beads. The incompatibility between these points of view was revealed by studies of closely linked genetic traits.

Under the above definitions two mutant genes would be considered *alleles* if they were so closely linked on the chromosome that crossing over never occurred between them. It would be expected that such genes would influence the same physiological function, although the effects would not necessarily be identical. In order to detect recombination between closely linked markers it is necessary to examine a very large number of progeny, since the frequency of the event is proportional to the distance separating the markers. When suitable test systems were devised it was found that nearly all independently arising mutations could be separated from one another by recombination, even though they occurred very close together on the same chromosome and there was no detectable difference in their physiological effects. It was also found that, if the distance as measured by frequency of recombination was established for each pair of mutants, the pairs could be arranged at specific points on a linear scale. In spite of the fact that all of the mutations seemed to affect the same phenotypic function, they were spread out physically over a segment of the chromosome. For this reason they have been referred to as *pseudoalleles*.

Understanding of the nature of pseudoalleles came when the idea of a gene as an indivisible unit was discarded. If the gene is seen as a functional unit consisting of a segment of a chromosome containing many smaller units arranged in a linear fashion, then there is no paradox. A mutation might affect only one of the smaller units, but a mutation in any one of the smaller units would interfere with the function of the segment as a whole. Recombination could occur among these mutational units within the functional segment, so that either normal or doubly mutant progeny would result. (See Fig. 2-9.)

Pseudoalleles have been studied in a number of organisms since the initial work in Drosophila. Bacteriophage, because it allows the handling of very large numbers of organisms, is a particularly useful tool in the study of genetic fine structure. The work of Benzer (1955, 1957, 1959) will serve to illustrate how much can be learned about the internal structure of the functional units generally embodied in the concept of "gene."

The bacteriophage T4 is a virus that infects some strains of *E. coli*, resulting in lysis of the host cell. If a dilute suspension of T4 is plated on an agar dish seeded with sensitive host cells, a clear plaque of lysed cells will appear wherever a bacteriophage particle originally landed. The size of each plaque will be about the same for a given combination of host cells and virus particles.

Occasionally plaques are observed that differ in size from the surrounding population. These represent heritable mutations in the virus particles. A number of mutations have been observed that result in plaques larger than the original "wild" type of strain. These have been designated as *r* mutants and can be further differentiated into three types depending on their ability to attack various host strains of *E. coli*. This is shown in Table 5, below. Linkage studies show that each of the three types is separated from the others on the viral chromosome. All of the mutants of a particular type are closely linked, however.

Benzer selected the *rII* series of mutants for intensive study. These mutants were further divisible into two groups on the basis of whether or not they could mutate back to the original wild type. The reverting mutants result from point mutations, so designated because the alteration of genetic material appears to affect only a single point (nucleotide pair?) on the chromosome.

If two different point mutants are grown together in the same host cell a normal offspring will occasionally be formed. This can happen either as a result of back mutation or in a manner analogous

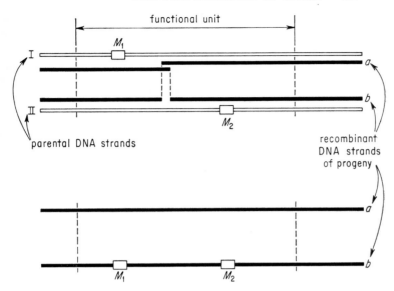

Fig. 2-9. Diagram illustrating recombination within a functional unit of a chromosome. Both parental chromosomes are defective because of the mutations M_1 and M_2. Two types of recombinants are possible. In a, neither mutation is represented in the daughter chromosome; hence, it should be able to function normally. In b, both mutations have been incorporated, and therefore it cannot function normally. The double mutant will not necessarily be distinguishable from I or II, but a should be recognizable. Recombination can occur either as a result of crossing over (diploid organisms) or of a copy-choice mechanism, although the diagram illustrates the latter.

Table 5

Formation of Plaques by r Mutants of Bacteriophage T4 on Three Strains of *E. coli*

r, mutant plaque; $+$, wild type plaque; $-$, does not grow. (From Benzer, 1957.)

Bacteriophage strain	*E. coli* strain		
	B	S	K
wild type	$+$	$+$	$+$
rI	r	r	r
rII	r	$+$	$-$
$rIII$	r	$+$	$+$

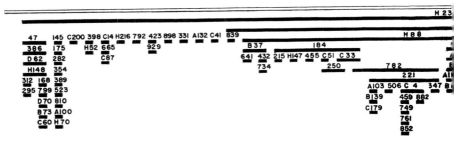

A cistron

Fig. 2-10. Map (above and facing) of some of the deletions of the *rII* locus in bacteriophage T4. Each deletion is designated by an arbitrarily assigned number. Cistrons *A* and *B* are functionally complementary. (From Benzer, 1959.)

to offspring *a* of Fig. 2-9. From the frequency of this event it is possible to obtain recombination values (distances) for any pair of mutants. These recombination values can be used to establish a unique linear arrangement of the mutants. By comparing the sum of the distances in a sequence of mutants and the total distance as measured directly, it can be shown that point (reverting) mutations do not appear to occupy much space on the chromosome.

Nonreverting mutants, on the other hand, do appear to affect a segment along the chromosome. Each such mutant can be defined by a series of consecutive point mutations with which it will not recombine. These nonreverting mutants can best be explained as deletions of genetic material rather than point alterations. They can be mapped, as shown in Fig. 2-10. If the deletions of a pair of mutants do not overlap, then normal recombinant offspring can be formed. If they do overlap, the absence of normal segments corresponding to the region of overlap makes normal recombinants impossible.

The *rII* mutants can also be separated into groups on the basis of whether or not they are functionally complementary. This is defined as the ability of two mutant particles, each unable to produce normal growth by itself, to give normal growth when present together in the same host cell. Thus, in Fig. 2-10 the *rII* region is divided into two segments, *A* and *B*. If a host culture is inoculated with two phage suspensions, each bearing a mutation in the *A*

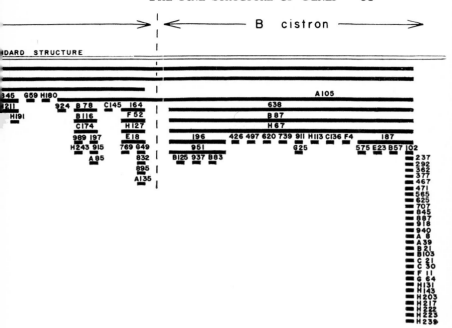

segment, then only mutant plaques will form—except for the rare recombinants that can form if the mutations do not overlap. But if one of the mutations is in the A region and the other in the B region, then normal plaques will form. These normal plaques will contain mixtures of the two mutant phage particles that will not have undergone chromosomal recombination. Such tests of complementariness are said to define regions of different function, called *cistrons* by Benzer.

The concept of complementation is perhaps more readily visualized in a diploid organism, such as Drosophila. Let us consider two phenotypically similar recessive mutations, a^- and b^-, corresponding to wild-type alleles a^+ and b^+. If a fly carries $a^- b^+$ on one chromosome and $a^+ b^-$ on the other and is normal, then the mutations are said to complement each other in the *trans position*. Both a^+ and b^+ are able to function regardless of mutation in the other position on the same chromosome. If the fly is mutant, then the mutations are noncomplementary and occur within the same functioning segment. In the latter case, if crossing over occurs between the two mutations to give a chromosomal configuration a^+b^+/a^-b^- (the *cis* arrangement), then the fly should *not* be mutant, because one chromosome is completely normal. Multiple infection of bacteria by viruses may be regarded as analogous to the diploid (or polyploid) phase of higher organisms.

It is possible that each cistron is associated ultimately with a different protein product, so that a particle having a mutation in A will produce normal enzyme B, while the particle that is mutant at B will produce normal enzyme A. The combination will produce both enzymes. It should be emphasized, however, that the recognition of these functionally independent segments is based entirely on their ability to complement each other when located in different chromosomes and not on the identification of products of the segments. Recent studies in other organisms, including Neurospora, indicate that complementation units in these organisms may be more complex than in phage and that the relatively simple picture based on studies of phage is not generally valid.

Benzer next focused attention on those point mutations that occur within the part of the chromosome covered by the $r164$ deletion. It is convenient to use deletions to define a certain segment of the chromosome. In this case $r164$ represents a deletion of material in the A cistron. He found 145 point mutations occurring within this segment, and, by the recombination techniques outlined above, they could be mapped at eleven different points. A diagram of the $r164$ region is shown in Fig. 2-11. The vast majority of the mutations occurred at the "hot spot," $r131$. Some aspect of the configuration of the DNA must lead to instability at this point. From the number of points that produced only a single mutant, it can be inferred that there are many other mutable points along the segment that did not happen to mutate during the time that mutants were being collected.

The mutants studied above were all spontaneous; that is, no agent was intentionally applied to the phage to increase the mutation rate. If a mutagenic agent is used, quite a different spectrum of mutations may be obtained. This is illustrated by the work of Benzer and Freese (1958), who used 5-bromouracil to induce mutations in the same system just described. When these mutants were mapped they were found not to coincide with the spontaneous mutants at all. A comparison of the spontaneous and induced spectra is shown in Fig. 2-12. At only three points were mutants recovered both from the spontaneous and induced experiments.

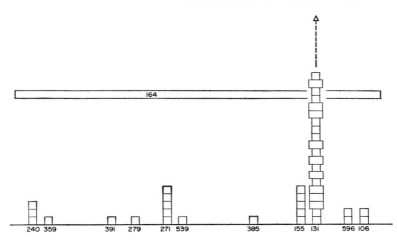

Fig. 2-11. A diagram of the spontaneous point mutations of the r164 segment of bacteriophage T4. Each position is designated by the first mutant located at that position. Each box represents an independently isolated mutant. The arrow at r131 indicates 103 additional mutants. (From Benzer, 1957.)

This is an excellent illustration of the specificity of mutation. Although the same functional unit may be affected by a variety of mutagenic agents, so that there is no phenotypic difference among the mutant products, it is also apparent that each mutagenic agent has some degree of specificity in its action. This specificity probably results from the fine structure of the DNA, that is, the sequence of nucleotides. Thus, 5-bromouracil, a thymine analog, would be expected to cause errors in replication of DNA at those points where thymine occurs. The existence of "hot spots" would suggest that the configuration of neighboring nucleotides may influence the probability of an error.

The study of mutational spectra is a most promising tool of genetics. (For example, see Freese, 1959.) It would seem that various mutagenic agents could be classified in a small number of categories based on specificity, each associated with some structural element of the DNA that it can affect most readily. If this is so, it may become possible to map chromosomes in terms of their sequence of nucleotides. Thus, genetics may be able to supply the answer to a problem that is basically chemical, but one for which chemistry still lacks sufficiently sensitive techniques.

It is now apparent, from a consideration of the structure of

DNA and its genetic function, why the different definitions of a gene are contradictory. The unit of function consists of a long segment of DNA. The unit of mutation, designated a *muton* by

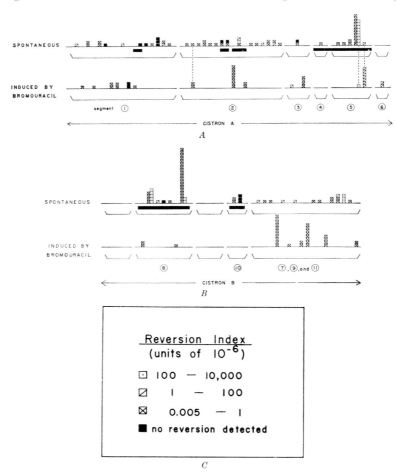

Fig. 2-12. A comparison of the maps of spontaneous and 5-bromouracil induced mutations at the *rII* locus of bacteriophage T4. The order of mutants within a segment has not been established. (From Benzer and Freese, 1958.)

Benzer, can consist of a single nucleotide pair. The smallest unit not divisible by recombination, a *recon*, probably consists of a single nucleotide pair, also.

THE REPLICATION OF DNA

One of the merits of the Watson-Crick structure of DNA, which gained it wide popularity among geneticists, was the possibility it offered for accurate gene replication. Watson and Crick (1953b) recognized shortly after the structure was elucidated that a simple model of DNA replication could be derived that satisfied all the known facts. Their model consisted in separation of the complementary strands, each of which would then serve as a template on which mononucleotides could align themselves in a specific sequence and polymerize. The newly polymerized strand would be complementary to its template and hence identical with the original partner of the template. A diagram of this model is shown in Fig. 2-13.

At the time this model was proposed there were no experimental means of testing its validity. Most scientists were reluctant to accept it, however, because of the difficulty of unwinding a structure as long as DNA was thought to be. For example, a piece of DNA of a molecular weight of 6 million (the accepted molecular weight at that time) would consist of approximately 10,000 nucleotide pairs. With 10 pairs per rotation of the helix, there would be 1000 turns in the molecule. Since the length of such a molecule would be 1000×34 Angstroms, or 3.4 microns, it would have to be rolled up in order to fit into most cells, and it would have to unwind and replicate while thus rolled up. In many cases this would have to take place in a few minutes.

Levinthal and Crane (1956) worked against this skepticism. They assumed that a DNA molecule is analogous to a flexible speedometer cable and would rotate throughout its entire length without changing its position in the surrounding medium. Under such circumstances, the energy required to rotate a molecule is found to be of a reasonable order of magnitude. Nevertheless, it is still difficult to visualize such a long structure replicating to give two separated daughter structures of equal complexity.

To overcome the unwinding problem, a number of models of DNA have been proposed as alternatives to the original single unbroken double helix. These models are generally modifications of the Watson-Crick structure, in which the molecule consists of subunits of double helices joined in various ways. During replication the subunits would come apart, presenting a less formidable

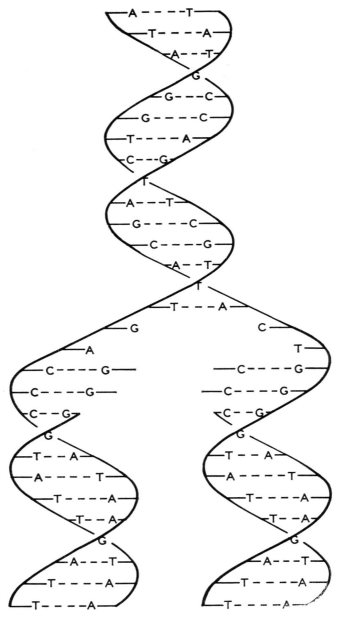

Fig. 2-13. Replication of a DNA molecule according to the suggestion of Watson and Crick (1953b). Note that each daughter helix consists of one newly synthesized strand and one parental strand.

unwinding problem. Should such subunits form during replication, they might reassociate so that the original parental relationship is retained, or they might reassociate in a random fashion. This is illustrated in Fig. 2-14. Finally, DNA might replicate in some manner not yet considered, involving no unwinding of the DNA at all. This last method would be conservative, in that the two products of replication would be the intact parental molecule and

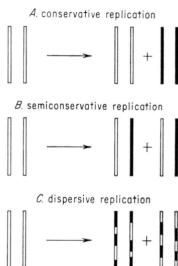

A. conservative replication

B. semiconservative replication

C. dispersive replication

Fig. 2-14. Theoretical modes of replication of DNA. The parental DNA is indicated with an open bar. The newly synthesized DNA is indicated by a solid bar.

one completely new molecule. The suggestion of Watson and Crick would result in a semiconservative method, since each parental strand would be intact after replication, but both would be paired with new strands. The subunit models might result in either semiconservative or dispersive replication, depending on whether they reassociated regularly or at random.

One of the first experiments dealing with this problem was performed by Levinthal and Thomas (1957), who worked with bacteriophage. They labeled phage particles intensively with P^{32} so that individual DNA molecules could be followed. By rupturing the phage particles with osmotic shock it was possible to obtain a suspension of DNA that could be spread on a microscope slide and used to prepare autoradiographs. The amount of P^{32} in each particle could be quantified by the number of tracks produced in film placed in contact with the slide.

When labeled bacteriophage was shocked before replication, the DNA was found either in large particles about 40 percent of the size of the total DNA in intact bacteriophage, or in small particles. When the phage was allowed to replicate once before shocking, the large particles contained only half of their original label, suggesting that each consisted of half parental and half new DNA. When the phage was allowed to replicate more than once, there were both labeled and unlabeled particles. Each of the labeled particles still contained half its original label.

The significance of the large versus the small pieces of DNA has still to be ascertained. If only the large piece of DNA in each phage is considered, then its replication is most consistent with the semiconservative mechanism. The original parental label is reduced by one half during one replication, but it does not undergo further reduction.

Another experiment was carried out by Taylor, Woods, and Hughes (1957). They studied seedlings of the broad bean *Vicia faba,* labeling its chromosomes with radioactive thymine. Since thymine goes only into DNA, it is possible to label DNA specifically by forming it in the presence of radioactive thymine, usually thymine in which the hydrogens have been partially replaced by tritium. With this technique it is possible to prepare autoradiographs of individual chromosomes. The results obtained with chromosomes of this higher plant are entirely in agreement with those of Levinthal. Both daughter chromosomes of a labeled parental chromosome carry tritium. The tritium is not further divided in succeeding replications, however.

Both these experiments rule out a dispersive method of replication. Although they are most compatible with the semiconservative, this involves the assumption that the large phage particle and the *Vicia faba* chromosomes are equivalent to DNA molecules. The first good evidence that this assumption is valid comes from recent studies by Meselson and Stahl (1958), using the technique of density gradient centrifugation. If a dense salt such as cesium chloride is placed in an ultracentrifuge, it will tend to concentrate at the bottom of the cell and form a solution whose density increases with depth. Large molecules of intermediate density, when added to the CsCl solution, will concentrate in a band at the position in the cell where the density of the molecules equals that of the CsCl. For example, the density of DNA is approximately 1.71, depending on the source. If a solution of CsCl is used with the density gradient in the ultracentrifuge varying from 1.65 to 1.75, then DNA will form a band at the point where the CsCl density is 1.71.

If DNA containing N^{15} is centrifuged, instead of DNA containing the usual N^{14}, the band forms at a position of greater density. Thus DNA labeled with N^{15} can be recognized by its density. Meselson and Stahl grew *E. coli* in N^{15} until most of the DNA consisted of heavy nitrogen. Then they transferred the growing cells to ordinary N^{14} medium and measured the density of the DNA at various times afterward. The results are shown in Fig. 2-15. They found that, at the time of transfer to N^{14}, all the DNA layered in a band corresponding to N^{15} DNA. Almost immediately, as new DNA was synthesized from N^{14}, there appeared a new band halfway between N^{15} and N^{14} DNA. At the end of one generation the hybrid DNA comprised all the DNA found. In succeeding generations pure N^{14} DNA appeared and the hybrid DNA became quantitatively smaller.

These results are most compatible with the semiconservative mode of replication. If the N^{15} DNA split into two pieces, each serving as a template for the condensation of an N^{14} strand, then one replication would yield an N^{15}/N^{14} hybrid DNA. An additional replication would yield a pure N^{14} and another hybrid. The pure N^{15} DNA would be destroyed by one replication, but the hybrid would persist throughout subsequent generations, although the relative amount would diminish. Meselson and Stahl were able to perform one more experiment indicating that the unit of DNA not reduced is indeed a single strand rather than some higher unit. Heating will denature DNA. It ruptures the hydrogen bonds, thereby destroying the double helix. In most cases the paired strands are so intertwined that they remain together, even though the regular pairing has been lost. In the case of *E. coli* DNA, the strands apparently can become separated during heating, as indicated by a reduction in molecular weight to half the original value. Meselson and Stahl heated some of the hybrid DNA of uniform density and produced two types of half molecules. One corresponded to a single strand N^{15} structure and the other to N^{14}. It seems then that the hybrid molecule double helix does in fact consist of one parental N^{15} strand and one newly synthesized N^{14} strand.

Impractical though it may seem, there is now little doubt that DNA unwinds into single strands during replication. A corollary

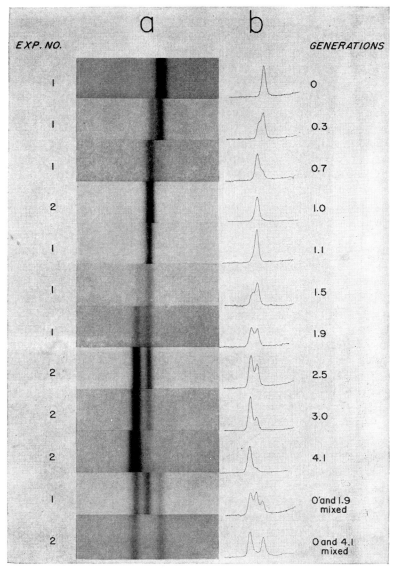

Fig. 2-15. The pattern of synthesis of DNA as revealed by ultracentrifugation in CsCl. The ultraviolet absorption photographs are given under *a*. The CsCl solution increases in density toward the right. Microdensitometer tracings are shown under *b*. At generation 0, the *E. coli* contained only N^{15} DNA. At the end of one generation on N^{14}, all of the DNA is hybrid N^{15}/N^{14}. After one generation, pure N^{14} DNA appears. (From Meselson and Stahl, 1958.)

of this is that individual strands of DNA remain intact during generations of replication. An exception is found in organisms in which crossing over occurs. Here a segment of a double helix may be exchanged during synapsis, resulting in a gradual dispersal of the original atoms.

In this section we have considered how strands of DNA could serve as templates for the condensation of nucleotides in a specific sequence. The formation of polynucleotide strands requires the formation of covalent bonds, which in turn requires that energy be supplied to the system. Knowledge of the biochemical steps involved in polynucleotide synthesis comes largely from the studies of Kornberg (1957) and his associates. They have demonstrated that synthesis of DNA requires three major components: a mixture of the triphosphates of the four DNA bases, an enzyme, and a primer. The primer, interestingly enough, consists of preformed DNA. The reaction can be pictured as follows:

$$A—dR—P—P—P + G—dR—P—P—P \xrightarrow[\text{primer}]{\text{enzyme, Mg}^{++}}$$

$$\begin{matrix} & & & G \\ & & & | \\ A—dR—P—dR—P—P—P + PP \end{matrix}$$

The reaction will not proceed unless the primer is present. Its role is apparently to furnish the template that directs the sequence of nucleotides. The enzyme, therefore, lacks specificity for determining the sequence of bases, and joins together whatever bases are brought into the correct steric configuration by the primer. This is borne out by the observation that the polynucleotide chains formed *in vitro* have the same ratio of bases as the primer used.

These biochemical studies fit exactly the picture of DNA synthesis as visualized on the basis of genetic and physical studies. As the double helix unwinds, the enzyme must sit near the point of unwinding, hooking together the nucleotides as they align themselves on the single strands. This is an amazingly accurate process. Nevertheless, an error is occasionally made because the wrong base manages to stay in position long enough to be hooked into the new chain by the enzymes. In such a case, a point mutation will have been produced.

GENERAL REFERENCES

BRACHET, J., 1957. *Biochemical Cytology,* New York: Academic Press. 516 pages.

PONTECORVO, G., 1958. *Trends in Genetic Analysis,* New York: Columbia University Press. 145 pages.

SWANSON, C. P., 1957. *Cytology and Cytogenetics,* Englewood Cliffs: Prentice Hall. 596 pages.

Structure and Function of Genetic Elements. Brookhaven Symposia in Biology: Number 12, 1959. Washington: Office of Technical Services, Department of Commerce. 187 pages.

LITERATURE CITED

AVERY, O. T., MACLEOD, C. M., and McCARTY, M., 1944. "Studies on the chemical nature of the substance inducing transformation of pneumoccoccal types," *Jour. Exptl. Med.,* **79,** 137–158.

BENZER, S., 1955. "Fine structure of a genetic region in bacteriophage," *Proc. Natl. Acad. Sci. U. S.,* **41,** 344–354.

———, 1957. "The elementary units of heredity," in *The Chemical Basis of Heredity* (McElroy, W. D., and Glass, B., eds.), Baltimore: The Johns Hopkins Press, pp. 70–93.

———, 1959. "On the topology of the genetic fine structure," *Proc. Natl. Acad. Sci. U. S.,* **45,** 1607–1620.

———, and FREESE, E., 1958. "Induction of specific mutations with 5-bromouracil," *Proc. Natl. Acad. Sci. U. S.,* **44,** 112–119.

CHARGAFF, E., 1955. "Isolation and composition of the deoxypentose nucleic acids and of the corresponding nucleoproteins," in *The Nucleic Acids, Vol. I* (Chargaff, E., and Davidson, J. N., eds.), New York: Academic Press, pp. 307–371.

CHU, E. H. Y., and GILES, N. H., 1959. "Human chromosome complements in normal somatic cells in culture," *Am. Jour. Human Genetics,* **11,** 63–79.

DAVISON, P. F., 1959. "The effect of hydrodynamic shear on the deoxyribonucleic acid from T_2 and T_4 bacteriophages," *Proc. Natl. Acad. Sci. U. S.,* **45,** 1560–1568.

FRAENKEL-CONRAT, H., SINGER, B. A., and WILLIAMS, R. C., 1957. "The nature of the progeny of virus reconstituted from protein and nucleic acid of different strains of tobacco mosaic virus," in *The Chemical Basis of Heredity* (McElroy, W. D., and Glass, B., eds.), Baltimore: The Johns Hopkins Press, pp. 501–512.

FREESE, E. "On the molecular explanation of spontaneous and induced mutations," *Brookhaven Symposia in Biology,* **12,** 63–75.

GIERER, A., and SCHRAMM, G., 1956. "Infectivity of ribonucleic acid from tobacco mosaic virus," *Nature,* **177,** 702–703.

GRIFFITH, F., 1928. "The significance of pneumococcal types," *Jour. Hyg.*, **27**, 113–159.

HALL, B. D., and SPIEGELMAN, S., 1961. "Sequence complementarity of T2-DNA and T2-specific RNA," *Proc. Natl. Acad. Sci. U. S.*, **47**, 137–146.

HERSHEY, A. D., and CHASE, M., 1952. "Independent functions of viral protein and nucleic acid in growth of bacteriophage," *Jour. Gen. Physiol.*, **36**, 39–56.

HOLLAENDER, A., and EMMENS, C. W., 1941. "Wavelength dependence of mutation production in the ultraviolet with special emphasis on fungi," *Cold Spring Harbor Symp. Quant. Biol.*, **9**, 179–185.

HOTCHKISS, R. D., 1952. "The role of desoxyribonucleates in bacterial transformations," in *Phosphorus Metabolism, Vol. II* (McElroy, W. D., and Glass, B., eds.), Baltimore: The Johns Hopkins Press, pp. 426–436.

KORNBERG, A., 1957. "Pathways of enzymatic synthesis of nucleotides and polynucleotides," in *The Chemical Basis of Heredity* (McElroy, W. D., and Glass, B., eds.), Baltimore: The Johns Hopkins Press, pp. 579–608.

LEUCHTENBERGER, C., LEUCHTENBERGER, R., and DAVIS, A. M., 1954. "A microspectrophotometric study of the desoxyribose nucleic acid (DNA) content in cells of normal and malignant human tissues," *Am. Jour. Pathol.*, **30**, 65–85.

LEVINTHAL, C., 1960. In *The First Conference on Genetics* (Sutton, H. E., ed.), New York: The Josiah Macy Jr. Foundation, p. 39.

——, and CRANE, H. R., 1956. "On the unwinding of DNA," *Proc. Natl. Acad. Sci. U. S.*, **42**, 436–438.

——, and THOMAS, C. A., JR., 1957. "The molecular basis of genetic recombination in phage," in *The Chemical Basis of Heredity* (McElroy, W. D., and Glass, B., eds.), Baltimore: The Johns Hopkins Press, pp. 737–743.

MESELSON, M., and STAHL, F. W., 1958. "The replication of DNA in *Escherichia coli,*" *Proc. Natl. Acad. Sci. U. S.*, **44**, 671–682.

SIMPSON, G. G., 1952. "How many species?" *Evolution,* **6**, 342.

SINSHEIMER, R. L., 1959. "Single-stranded deoxyribonucleic acid from bacteriophage ϕX174," *Jour. Mol. Biol.*, **1**, 43–53.

TAYLOR, J. H., WOODS, P. S., and HUGHES, W. L., 1957. "The organization and duplication of chromosomes as revealed by autoradiographic studies using tritium-labeled thymidine," *Proc. Natl. Acad. Sci. U. S.*, **43**, 122–128.

THORELL, B., 1955. "Nucleic acids in chromosomes and mitotic division," in *The Nucleic Acids, Vol. II* (Chargaff, E., and Davidson, J. N., eds.), New York: Academic Press, pp. 181–198.

VENDRELY, R., 1955. "The deoxyribonucleic acid content of the nucleus," in *The Nucleic Acids, Vol. II* (Chargaff, E., and Davidson, J. N., eds.), New York: Academic Press, pp. 155–180.

WATSON, J. D., and CRICK, F. H. C., 1953a. "A structure for deoxyribose nucleic acids," *Nature,* **171**, 737–738.

——, ——, 1953b. "Genetic implications of the structure of deoxyribonucleic acid," *Nature,* **171**, 964–967.

WILKINS, M. H. F., 1956. "Physical studies of the molecular structure of deoxyribose nucleic acid and nucleoprotein," *Cold Spring Harbor Symp. Quant. Biol.*, **21**, 75–88.

chapter three Protein Structure
and Specificity

Although the ultimate repository of information for cellular functions may be DNA, there is no case known in which DNA itself participates in a reaction of intermediary metabolism. This function is performed by the thousands of proteins in every cell. Most of the proteins serve as catalysts, lowering the energy barrier between some substrate S and product P_1 and thereby causing S to be converted into P_1 rather than accumulating or forming some other product P_2. Proteins derive their ability as specific catalysts from their structure. If that structure is altered, the catalytic activity may be lost or its specificity may be altered.

From the studies of Neurospora mutants it has been possible to relate genetic changes to changes in protein activities. Much of the early work on the genetic control of metabolism was done by Beadle and Tatum, who are identified with the formulation of the "one gene–one enzyme" theory. Briefly stated, this theory is that each gene controls the structure of one enzyme, and, conversely, that each enzyme is regulated by a single gene. The theory has been somewhat modified in recent years, but its essential correctness remains unchallenged.

In order to consider the changes in proteins that can be induced by gene mutation it will first be necessary to review some of the facts of protein structure.

44

Primary structure

Proteins consist of long chains of amino acids hooked together by peptide bonds, as shown. This covalent structure is generally referred to as the *primary structure* of the protein.

$$\underbrace{H_2N-\overset{\overset{\displaystyle R_1}{|}}{C}H-\overset{\overset{\displaystyle O}{\|}}{C}}_{\text{N-terminal}}-\overset{H}{N}-\overset{\overset{\displaystyle R_2}{|}}{C}H-\overset{\overset{\displaystyle O}{\|}}{C}-\overset{H}{N}-\overset{\overset{\displaystyle R_3}{|}}{C}H-\cdots$$

N-terminal
residue

$$\cdots-\overset{\overset{\displaystyle O}{\|}}{C}-\overset{H}{N}-\overset{\overset{\displaystyle R_{n-1}}{|}}{C}H-\overset{\overset{\displaystyle O}{\|}}{C}-\overset{H}{N}-\underbrace{\overset{\overset{\displaystyle R_n}{|}}{C}H-\overset{\overset{\displaystyle O}{\|}}{C}-OH}_{\text{C-terminal}}$$

C-terminal
residue

Some forty or more amino acids are known to occur in nature. Many of them are metabolic intermediates and are not found as constituents of proteins. Some 24 to 25 amino acids have actually been isolated from protein hydrolyzates. In the case of some amino acids, such as hydroxylysine and hydroxyproline, the introduction of a functional group onto the parent amino acid is thought to occur after that amino acid is incorporated into a polypeptide chain. Thus, with regard to specifying the original amino acid sequence in the chain, these secondarily formed amino acids would enter as the parent amino acid. The number of amino acids thought to enter into the formation of polypeptide chains is twenty. These are listed in Table 6.

The length of polypeptide chains varies among proteins. Ribonuclease, the smallest protein known other than the polypeptide hormones, has a molecular weight of 13,500 and consists of a single chain of 124 amino acids. By a combination of degradative procedures, it has been possible to establish the sequence of amino acids in ribonuclease, as shown in Fig. 3-1. The amino acid sequence of the protein of tobacco mosaic virus has also recently been reported (Tsugita, *et al.*, 1960). The other proteins whose primary structure has been elucidated are actually polypeptide hormones, which are smaller than enzymes and probably not strictly analogous functionally.

Table 6

The Amino Acids Found in Proteins

All of the amino acids are of the L configuration. Various other amino acids have been reported to occur in proteins. In some cases the findings have not been confirmed; in others the amino acid is a derivative of one listed below and is thought to be formed after the parent amino acid is already incorporated.

Amino acid	Abbreviation	Amino acid	Abbreviation
1. Alanine	Ala	11. Leucine	Leu
2. Arginine	Arg	12. Lysine	Lys
3. Aspartic acid	Asp	13. Methionine	Met
4. Asparagine	$Asp(NH_2)$ or An	14. Phenylalanine	Phe
5. Cysteine	Cys	15. Proline	Pro
6. Glutamic acid	Glu	16. Serine	Ser
7. Glutamine	$Glu(NH_2)$ or Gn	17. Threonine	Thr
8. Glycine	Gly	18. Tryptophan	Try
9. Histidine	His	19. Tyrosine	Tyr
10. Isoleucine	Ileu	20. Valine	Val

In nearly every case a given protein obtained from members of a single species is found to give a unique sequence of amino acids. To some extent this no doubt reflects genetic homogeneity at the locus controlling the synthesis of the protein. On the other hand, chemical studies of primary structure have rarely been designed to pick up variation present in a minority of individuals. Where inter-species differences do exist they can be associated with specific amino acid substitutions in the polypeptide chain. This is illustrated in Fig. 3-2.

These proteins are among the smallest known. Many proteins are ten times as large and a few are even larger. Some of the larger proteins are now known to consist of subunits, so that the "average protein unit" that must be synthesized may rarely exceed a molecular weight of approximately 20,000.

Secondary structure

An expanded polypeptide chain, such as those shown in the preceding section and in Fig. 3-1, occurs in nature only as a result

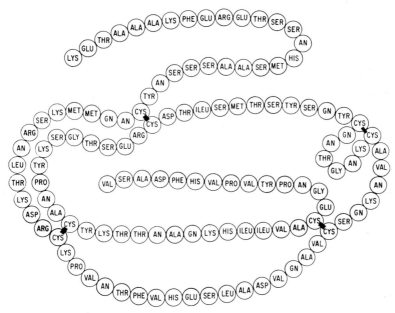

Fig. 3-1. The primary structure of the protein *ribonuclease* from bovine pancreas. The four disulfide bridges (Cys-Cys) are probably as indicated. A number of individuals have contributed to the elucidation of this structure, including Drs. C. H. W. Hirs, S. Moore, W. H. Stein, D. Spackman, and L. Bailey of the Rockefeller Institute and Drs. R. Redfield, J. Cooke, A. Ryle, and C. B. Anfinsen of the National Heart Institute. (From Anfinsen, 1959; 2d printing, 1960.)

... CySO$_3$H.Ala.Ser.Val	... (beef)
... CySO$_3$H.Thr.Ser.Ileu	... (pig)
... CySO$_3$H.Ala.Gly.Val	... (sheep)
... CySO$_3$H.Thr.Gly.Ileu	... (horse)
... CySO$_3$H.Thr.Ser.Ileu	... (sperm whale)
... CySO$_3$H.Ala.Ser.Thr	... (sei whale)

Fig. 3-2. Amino acid sequences in the peptide fragment of insulins showing species variation. The remaining 47 amino acids are identical in these species. (From Anfinsen, 1959.)

of denaturation. Even denatured proteins probably exist in this form only temporarily or partially. A much more stable configuration is obtained if the polypeptide chain is formed into a helix so that successive turns will form hydrogen bonds with one another. In this case the hydrogen bonds are between the hydrogen of the peptide nitrogen and the oxygen of the carbonyl. The formulation of these secondary structures is largely the work of Pauling and Corey (1951). Several structures have been found to be both energetically and sterically possible. The most important of these in globulins are the α helices. A polypeptide can be arranged into either a right- or left-handed helix. The most stable configuration contains 3.7 amino acid residues per turn of the helix, with a distance of 5.4 A between succeeding turns. This kind of configuration is illustrated in Fig. 3-3. The R groups of the amino acids project out from the principal axis of the helix.

Not all the amino acid residues in a polypeptide chain are part of a helical structure. For example, proline, whose amino nitrogen is part of a ring structure, cannot fit sterically into the left-handed α helix. Consequently, there is a discontinuity in the secondary structure associated with any proline residue. There may also be regions in which the interactions between chains are stronger than hydrogen bonds of a helix. This would be true when covalent disulfide bridges are formed between cysteine residues. At these points the helix may not be able to form. The regular α helix may then be regarded as a prominent feature of protein structure, but one that, in enzymes or other globular proteins, is limited to certain regions of the polypeptide chain.

Tertiary structure

Although a few proteins may occur as long thin rods, most of the enzymes are globular proteins. As such they are spherical or ellipsoidal, the α helices being folded into a more complex structure, the *tertiary* structure. This folding varies among proteins, and the stable configurations depend on the types and positions of the side chains of the individual amino acids. For example, two cysteine residues can react to form a disulfide bridge, stabilizing the tertiary structure. In addition, ionic and hydrogen bonds may add to the stability of the configuration. Interruptions of the secondary helix

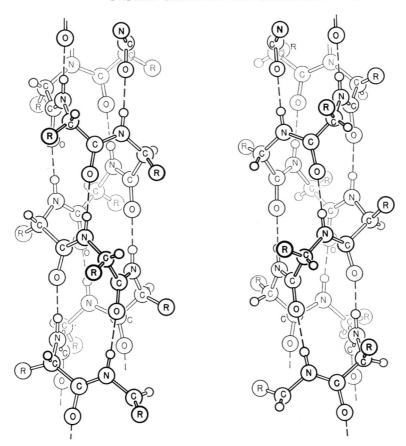

Fig. 3-3. Diagrams of protein helices. Both secondary structures are α helices, one being left-handed, the other right-handed. They are not mirror images, however, since each amino acid residue is in the L configuration. (From Pauling, 1960.)

by a proline residue are thought to be important in determining the tertiary configuration.

The ability to form these intramolecular bonds depends, of course, on the primary structure of the polypeptide chain. For any given sequence of amino acids there is probably more than one tertiary structure with some degree of stability. Only rarely would more than one form show maximum stability. It cannot be assumed that the most stable configuration is always the one with biological activity. If it were, however, it would be advantageous to the organism, since it would require less protein synthesis. The correct form of the tertiary structure can be determined solely by the primary structure, as has been demonstrated with ribonuclease (Sela, et al., 1957; Anfinsen, 1959, 1960). If native ribonuclease is treated with urea and sulfhydryl reagents, the disulfide bonds are broken and the protein unfolds into an inactive linear structure. If oxygen is bubbled slowly through a solution of this denatured ribonuclease, the disulfide bonds reform and the enzymatic activity returns. An interesting feature of this renaturation is that the disulfide bonds appear to reform just as in the original molecule. Thus, the position of even these covalent bonds is a natural consequence of the primary structure and does not require information from the gene. The conditions under which protein is synthesized intracellularly may facilitate the formation of certain tertiary structures. Nevertheless, the meager evidence existing points to the important role of the primary amino acid sequence in the determination of final configuration.

GENETIC CONTROL OF PROTEIN STRUCTURE

Three different levels of protein structure have been presented. Ultimately the function of a protein depends on the shape of the molecule and the distribution of charges and other functional groups on its surface. We know that gene mutations can change a protein. But what aspect of the structure is altered by mutation? A gene might control either the primary sequence of amino acids or the way in which the polypeptide chain folds up. A gene might even influence the secondary structure, although in general this would seem to be determined only by the amino acid sequences.

The abnormal hemoglobins

The genetically controlled protein system about which most is known is human hemoglobin. For several decades a disease known as sickle cell anemia has been recognized among certain populations. As briefly mentioned in Chapter 1, this disease is characterized by erythrocytes that function more or less normally in the presence of adequate oxygen. If the oxygen pressure is low, however, the erythrocytes assume highly abnormal shapes with long projections. When such cells are formed intravascularly they tend to slow down circulation, which in turn lowers the oxygen pressure and produces more sickling. A high rate of hemolysis may result from this sickling. The individuals afflicted with the disease show a variety of symptoms, all originating ultimately from the hemoglobin abnormality. This is illustrated in Fig. 1-2. It is a severe disease, usually fatal before the age of reproduction.

In addition to the severe form of the disease, there is a mild form which is benign. The patient's erythrocytes can be induced to sickle under laboratory conditions, but sickling does not occur *in vivo*. Hence, there is no interference with normal circulation. This type of individual is said to have sickle cell trait.

Sickle cell disease or trait tends to occur in certain families, and primarily among Negroes. It was therefore assumed to be inherited. In 1949 Neel reported that individuals with sickle cell disease are homozygous for a gene for which individuals with the sickle cell trait are heterozygous. Thus, both parents of a person with sickle cell disease would have sickle cell trait. If the normal gene is designated A and the abnormal gene S, the genotype of a normal person would be A/A, that of a person with sickle cell trait A/S, and a patient with sickle cell disease S/S.

Also in 1949 Pauling, Itano, Singer, and Wells reported a chemical difference in the hemoglobin from sickle cell patients as compared with normals. They found that, at alkaline pH, sickle cell hemoglobin migrates toward the anode more slowly than does normal hemoglobin. Furthermore, a person of genotype A/S possesses two kinds of hemoglobin, one corresponding to normal and one corresponding to sickle cell hemoglobin. Hemoglobin from these three types of individuals is shown in Fig. 3-4.

This finding from Pauling's laboratory was of paramount significance, since it was the first example of an inherited change in molecular structure. The metabolic blocks that had been studied prior to that time had been losses in the activity of an enzyme, but such losses were thought to represent an absence of the enzyme rather than an alteration of the protein molecule. To be sure, a change in electrophoretic mobility might possibly result from several types of alteration in a molecule. It might represent a change

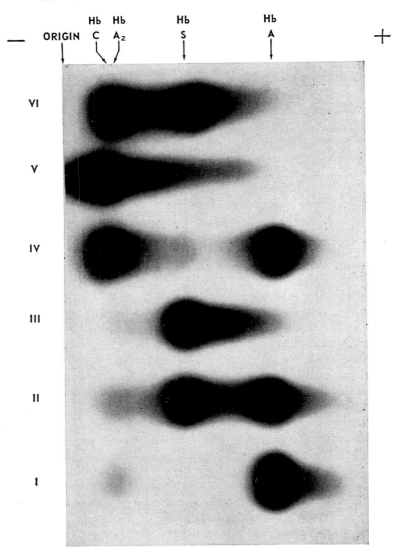

Fig. 3-4. Separation of hemoglobins by starch block electrophoresis, pH 8.6. Hemolyzates of washed erythrocytes were run. I: Normal adult blood, showing principally Hb A with a trace of Hb A₂. II: Sickle cell trait, showing both Hb A and Hb S. III: Sickle cell disease, with Hb S as the only major component. IV: Hb C/Hb A heterozygote. V: Homozygous Hb C. VI: Hb S/Hb C disease. (Courtesy of Dr. Donald L. Rucknagel.)

in the amino acid composition of the molecule; it might represent a difference in the way the polypeptide chains are folded, with different ionizable groups exposed on the surface; or it might represent a difference in the molecular size (degree of aggregation). Amino acid analyses of the whole purified hemoglobins failed to show any significant differences. The methods were such, however, that changes of one or a few amino acids would probably have gone undetected.

Since this discovery of hemoglobin S, a number of other hemoglobins have been discovered with electrophoretic mobilities different from normal hemoglobin A. With few exceptions these have been designated with letters of the alphabet in the sequence of their discovery. The first abnormal hemoglobin other than S was Hb C, discovered in 1951 by Kaplan, Zuelzer, and Neel. The total number of recognized abnormal hemoglobins currently totals about two dozen. No hemoglobin other than S has been found to produce sickling, although many of the other abnormal hemoglobins are associated with anemias of greater or lesser severity.

It will be profitable to review some of the facts of hemoglobin structure, in order to understand the effects of mutation on it. It is a globular protein of molecular weight 66,200. In addition to the protein portion, there are four porphyrin rings (hemes) in the molecule, each of which is complexed with one atom of iron. Studies of the N-terminal (free amino) amino acid residues revealed four such terminals, two beginning valyl-leucyl- and two beginning valyl-histidyl-leucyl- (Rhinesmith, *et al.*, 1957, 1958). It was postulated, and this seems now to be correct, that a molecule of hemoglobin consists of four polypeptide chains, two of one type and two of another. The chain beginning valyl-leucyl- is arbitrarily designated α, and the valyl-histidyl-leucyl- is β. Each of these chains consists of about 140 amino acids, and each is attached to a heme. By carefully lowering the pH, the hemoglobin tetramer can be made to dissociate into two dimers. The dissociation is into two unlike units and is reversible (Itano and Singer, 1958).

$$\alpha_2\beta_2 \rightleftharpoons \alpha_2 + \beta_2$$

It is sometimes useful to indicate the hemoglobin molecule as a tetramer $\alpha_2\beta_2$.

The true nature of the alteration in Hb S was demonstrated

by Ingram (1956). Using modifications of techniques developed by Sanger, he broke hemoglobin into small fragments by trypsin digestion. Trypsin is a proteolytic enzyme that hydrolyzes peptide bonds formed from the carboxyl of either lysine or arginine. In Hb A there are about 52 such bonds, but, since each of the α and β chains occurs twice, there would actually be only 26 different bonds. The breaking of 26 such bonds located in two different chains would give 28 peptide fragments, each consisting on the average of ten amino acids.

By using a combination of paper chromatography and electrophoresis it is possible to separate a mixture of peptides. Applying this technique to Hb's A and S, Ingram found that the two hemoglobins give identical peptide patterns ("fingerprints"), with one exception. One peptide, arbitrarily designated No. 4 in Hb A, is missing in Hb S. Instead, a peptide is present with different migration rates. The fingerprints of Hb's A and S are shown in Fig. 3-5.

These peptides were then eluted from the fingerprints and studied for amino acid composition and sequence. In the case of Hb A, No. 4 peptide has the following structure:

$$\text{Val.His.Leu.Thr.Pro.Glu.Glu.Lys.}$$
$$+ \quad + \qquad\qquad - \quad - \quad +-$$

The plus and minus signs indicate the charges the amino acid residues are capable of assuming under various conditions of pH. In the case of Hb S, peptide No. 4 was found to have the structure

$$\text{Val.His.Leu.Thr.Pro.Val.Glu.Lys.}$$
$$+ \quad + \qquad\qquad\qquad - \quad +-$$

The only difference is the substitution of valine for glutamic acid in position No. 6. This substitution provides the molecule with one less amino acid capable of releasing a proton and accounts for the difference in migration of the two hemoglobins. Since this difference occurs twice in each molecule, the total charge difference is $+2$.

Hemoglobin C has an even greater positive charge than Hb S. When it was fingerprinted it, too, was found to vary only in peptide 4 (Hunt and Ingram, 1958). The amino acid sequence of peptide 4 in Hb C is

$$\text{Val.His.Leu.Thr.Pro.Lys.Glu.Lys.}$$
$$+ \quad + \qquad\qquad + \quad - \quad +-$$

Here the substitution of lysine for glutamic acid results in a net

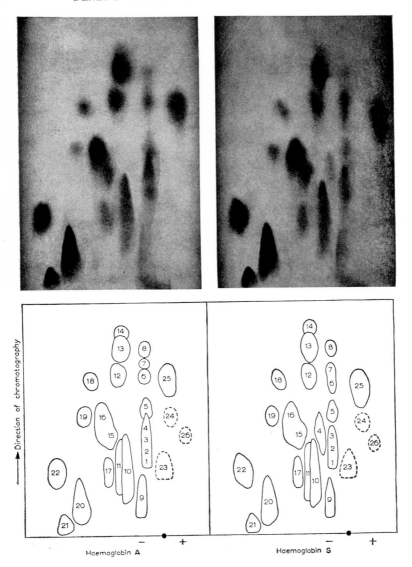

Fig. 3-5. Peptide fingerprints of hemoglobins A and S. The hemoglobins were first digested with trypsin; then the peptides were subjected to electrophoresis, followed by paper chromatography at right angles. Dotted lines indicate peptides that are visible only after heating. Only peptide No. 4 was found to differ in the two hemoglobins. (From Ingram, 1958.)

charge difference of $+2$ per peptide, or $+4$ per molecule. Several of the other abnormal hemoglobins have been fingerprinted and have shown single amino acid differences in other peptides. All three samples of Hb D that were fingerprinted proved to be different in different peptides (Benzer, *et al.,* 1958). This emphasizes the fact that electrophoretic mobility tends to reflect total charge differences, but it cannot be used as evidence for molecular identity. Since the molecules will primarily vary by unit differences in charge, they will tend to fall into certain discrete categories. The actual migration may vary slightly within these categories, but true identity must be established by additional studies, such as fingerprinting.

By using C^{14}-leucine-labeled hemoglobin it has been possible to establish that the defects in Hb's S and C are located in the β chain (Vinograd, *et al.,* 1959). It is now thought that peptide No. 4 is the N-terminal peptide of the β chain. Some of the abnormal hemoglobins have been found to involve substitutions in the α chain. One unusual hemoglobin, Hb H, consists of 4 β chains (Jones, *et al.,* 1959a). Whether these are normal β's has not been determined. A β_4 molecule has not been detected in normal individuals.

Since the amino acid substitutions of the inherited abnormal hemoglobins can be assigned to one or the other chain, it is convenient to designate the molecular structure with superscripts to indicate the constitution of each chain. For example, normal hemoglobin, Hb A, can be symbolized as $\alpha_2^A\beta_2^A$. Hemoglobin S is $\alpha_A\beta_2^S$, and Hb C is $\alpha_2^A\beta_2^C$. Hb I, which has a substitution in the α chain, is $\alpha_2^I\beta_2^A$. It should be possible to have a hemoglobin with substitutions in both chains, and such a case is known. Hemoglobin Ho-2 (Hopkins-2) is defective in the α chain, and the double heterozygote molecule $\alpha_2^{Ho-2}\beta_2^S$ has been detected (Itano, 1960). A summary of the established defects in hemoglobin structure is given in Fig. 3-6.

The designations in the previous paragraph are for hemoglobin molecules only; they do not represent the genetic constitution of the individuals who possess them. There are thought to be two loci controlling the synthesis of adult hemoglobin. (See the review by Rucknagel and Neel, 1961, for a detailed discussion of points covered in this section.) For several reasons, only two loci would be desirable. The first is that there are only two types of polypeptide chains in hemoglobin. It would be tidy to have each locus con-

ALPHA CHAIN

Position:	1	2	16	30	57	58	68	141
	Val.	Leu.	...Lys.	...Glu.	...Gly.	His.	...An	...Arg

Hb Variant

Hb I	.Asp.							
Hb G$_{Honolulu}$			.Gn .					
Hb Norfolk				.Asp.				
Hb M$_{Boston}$						.Tyr.		
Hb G$_{Philadelphia}$							.Lys.	

BETA CHAIN

Position:	1	2	3	6	7	26	63	67	125	146
	Val.	His.	Leu.	...Glu.	Glu.	...Glu.	...His.	...Val.	...Glu.	...His

Hb Variant

Hb S			.Val.							
Hb C			.Lys.							
Hb G$_{San\ Jose}$				.Gly.						
Hb E					.Lys.					
Hb M$_{Saskatoon}$							.Tyr.			
Hb M$_{Milwaukee-1}$								.Glu.		
Hb D$_{\beta\ Punjab}$(D$_\gamma$)									.Gn .	

Fig. 3-6. A summary of the established amino acid substitutions in human hemoglobin variants. The complete amino acid sequence of the two chains is largely known, through the efforts of Braunitzer, *et al.* (1960a, 1960b), and Hill and Konigsberg (1961). References for the amino acid substitutions are as follows: Hb's S and C, Hunt and Ingram (1958); Hb E, Hunt and Ingram (1959); Hb G$_{San\ Jose}$, Hill, Swenson, and Schwartz (1960); Hb G$_{Philadelphia}$, Baglioni and Ingram (1961); Hb I, Murayama (1960); Hb Norfolk, Baglioni (1961); Hb D$_{\beta Punjab}$, C. Baglioni (unpublished); Hb's M$_{Boston}$, M$_{Saskatoon}$ (= M$_{Emory}$), and M$_{Milwaukee-1}$, Park Gerald, Mary Efron, and Anthony Pisciotta (unpublished); and Hb G$_{Honolulu}$ (= G$_{Greenwich}$ and G$_{Singapore}$), Robert T. Swenson and Robert L. Hill (unpublished). The author wishes to thank those authors who gave permission to use their unpublished results and Dr. Vernon Ingram for making available some of the material of this figure.

trol the synthesis of one type of chain. On this assumption it has been suggested that the genotype for Hb A be designated Hb^A_α/Hb^A_α, Hb^A_β/Hb^A_β. A person of this genotype would produce Hb $\alpha^A_2\beta^A_2$. A person with sickle cell trait would have genotype Hb^A_α/Hb^A_α, Hb^A_β/Hb^S_β and would produce Hb's $\alpha^A_2\beta^A_2$ and $\alpha^A_2\beta^S_2$. One with sickle cell disease would be Hb^A_α/Hb^A_α, Hb^S_β/Hb^S_β and would produce only $\alpha^A_2\beta^S_2$.

For reasons that are not known, the unit of synthesis of hemoglobin is the dimer, that is, the basic unit appears to be α_2 chains rather than α chains. This is indicated by the failure to find mixed molecules of the type $\alpha_2^A \beta^A \beta^S$. A heterozygote of genotype Hb_α^A/Hb_α^A, Hb_β^A/Hb_β^S would seem to have the constitution necessary for the formation of this kind of molecule if individual chains were produced independently. Yet such a heterozygote produces $\alpha_2^A \beta_2^A$ and $\alpha_2^A \beta_2^S$, but not $\alpha_2^A \beta^A \beta^S$. Various schemes have been proposed to account for the absence of the mixed molecule, but there is no experimental evidence as yet that bears on this point.

In addition to Hb A, the major component in a normal adult, several other types of hemoglobin are known. The one most studied is fetal hemoglobin (Hb F). This is the hemoglobin that occurs primarily in the fetus and slowly disappears in the newborn, decreasing to a small percentage of the total hemoglobin by the time the infant is several months of age. In anemias due to certain abnormal hemoglobins, Hb F may persist at increased levels throughout life. This hemoglobin can be differentiated from adult hemoglobin because it is much more resistant to denaturation by alkali. Its electrophoretic mobility is similar to, but usually distinguishable from, adult hemoglobin. The amino acid composition of fetal hemoglobin is distinctly different from that of Hb A. Recent studies indicate that Hb F, too, is composed of two types of chains (Schroeder and Matsuda, 1958). One of them appears to be identical with the α chain of Hb A and the other is analogous to the β chain of Hb A, but with amino acid differences at a number of places (Hunt, 1959; Jones, et al., 1959b). The second chain has been designated γ, giving a molecular structure for Hb F of $\alpha_2^A \gamma_2^F$. The γ chain is presumably controlled by a third genetic locus. The α chain may be controlled by the same locus that controls the α chain of Hb A.

A third hemoglobin that has been studied is Hb A_2. This is a normal minor constituent and is shown in Fig. 3-4. It appears to be increased in some anemias caused by hemoglobin abnormalities, but it always remains a minor constituent. It has also been found to possess the same α chain as Hb's A and F (Schroeder, 1960). The rest of the molecule is composed of a fourth type of chain, designated δ. Thus the structure of Hb A_2 is $\alpha_2^A \delta_2^{A_2}$.

The structural relationships of these three hemoglobin molecules raise interesting questions as to their role in development and in evolution. It is particularly interesting that one locus, the Hb_α locus, may be responsible for products going into three different molecules.

From these studies on hemoglobin it is apparent that gene mutation affects the primary amino acid sequence of proteins. Furthermore, evidence has been presented that the primary structure determines the tertiary structure. One exception generally cited is that of immune antibodies. The more popular theories of antibody production have assumed that a protein "blank" somehow is directed during folding so that it assumes a configuration complementary to the specific antigen.

Lederberg (1959) has recently summarized arguments for the idea that even in antibodies the tertiary structure is determined solely by the amino acid sequence and that each species of antibody therefore differs in its primary structure. Rather than have each cell possess the information for all possible antibodies, Lederberg would have one highly mutable locus that would be present in many different forms in the somatic cells (lymphoid tissue) that constitute the antibody-producing apparatus. Injection of an antigen would stimulate proliferation of those cells already capable of producing antibodies with the necessary specificity. The information for antibody specificity would already have been present in the host organism, a point on which this theory differs from most others. Should this theory prove valid, the only major exception to the primacy of primary structure will have been disposed of.

Not all mutations result in an altered protein product. Many result in no product at all. It is not always easy to distinguish between absence of a product and presence of one that has lost its functions. In some cases, where the product can be characterized by multiple criteria, such as enzymatic activity, immunological activity, or behavior during purification, a product is detected by one of the latter two criteria even when no enzymic activity can be detected. In other cases a loss of activity is accompanied by a loss of product by all criteria. Examples will be discussed further in the following chapter.

LITERATURE CITED

ANFINSEN, C. B., 1959. *The Molecular Basis of Evolution,* New York: John Wiley and Sons.

————, 1960. In *The First Conference on Genetics* (Sutton, H. E., ed.), New York: Josiah Macy, Jr. Foundation, pp. 77–78.

BAGLIONI, C., 1961. "Chemistry of hemoglobin Norfolk, a rare variant of human hemoglobin," *Fed. Proc.,* **20,** 254.

————, and INGRAM, V. M., 1961. "Four adult haemoglobin types in one person," *Nature,* **189,** 465–467.

BENZER, S., INGRAM, V. M., and LEHMANN, H., 1958. "Three varieties of human haemoglobin D," *Nature,* **182,** 852–854.

BRAUNITZER, G., HILSCHMANN, N., HILSE, K., LIEBOLD, B., and MÜLLER, R., 1960a. "Die Konstitution der β-Kette der Hauptkomponente des normalen adulten Humanhämoglobins," *Z. physiol. Chem.,* **322,** 96–100.

————, RUDLOFF, V., HILSE, K., LIEBOLD, B., and MÜLLER, R., 1960b. "Eine Partialformel der α-Kette der Hauptkomponente des adulten menschlichen Hämoglobins," *Z. physiol. Chem.,* **320,** 283–288.

HILL, R. J., and KONIGSBERG, W., 1961. "The partial structural formula of the α-chain of human hemoglobin," *J. Biol. Chem.,* **236,** PC7–8.

————, SWENSON, R. T., and SCHWARTZ, H. C., 1960. "Characterization of a chemical abnormality in hemoglobin G," *J. Biol. Chem.,* **235,** 3182–3187.

HUNT, J. A., 1959. "Identity of the α-chains of adult and foetal human haemoglobin," *Nature,* **183,** 1373.

————, and INGRAM, V. M., 1958. "Allelomorphism and the chemical differences of the human hemoglobins A, S, and C," *Nature,* **181,** 1062–1063.

————, and INGRAM, V. M., 1959. "Human haemoglobin E: The chemical effect of gene mutation," *Nature,* **184,** 870–872.

INGRAM, V. M., 1956. "A specific chemical difference between the globins of normal human and sickle-cell anaemia haemoglobin," *Nature,* **178,** 792–794.

————, 1958. "Abnormal human haemoglobins. I. The comparison of normal human and sickle-cell haemoglobins by 'fingerprinting,' " *Biochim. Biophys. Acta,* **28,** 539–545.

ITANO, H. A., 1960. In *The First Conference on Genetics* (Sutton, H. E., ed.), New York: Josiah Macy, Jr. Foundation, pp. 137–138.

————, and SINGER, S. J., 1958. "Dissociation and recombination of human adult hemoglobins A, S, and C," *Proc. Natl. Acad. Sci. U. S.,* **44,** 522–529.

JONES, R. T., SCHROEDER, W. A., BALOG, J. E., and VINOGRAD, J. R., 1959a. "Gross structure of hemoglobin H," *Jour. Am. Chem. Soc.,* **81,** 3161.

————, ————, and VINOGRAD, J. R., 1959b. "Identity of the α-chains of hemoglobins A and F," *Jour. Am. Chem. Soc.,* **81,** 4749–4750.

KAPLAN, E., ZUELZER, W. W., and NEEL, J. V., 1951. "A new inherited abnormality of hemoglobin and its interaction with sickle-cell hemoglobin," *Blood,* **6,** 1240–1259.

LEDERBERG, J., 1959. "Genes and antibodies," *Science,* **129,** 1649–1653.

MURAYAMA, M., 1960. "The chemical difference between normal human hemoglobin and hemoglobin I," *Fed. Proc.,* **19,** 78.

NEEL, J. V., 1949. "The inheritance of sickle-cell anemia," *Science,* **110,** 64–66.

PAULING, L., 1960. *The Nature of the Chemical Bond,* 3d ed., Ithaca: Cornell Univ. Press, p. 500.

————, and COREY, R. B., 1951. *Proc. Natl. Acad. Sci. U. S.,* **37,** 235–285.

————, ITANO, H. A., SINGER, S. J., and WELLS, I. C., 1949. "Sickle-cell anemia, a molecular disease," *Science,* **110,** 543–548.

RHINESMITH, H. S., SCHROEDER, W. A., and MARTIN, N., 1958. "The N-terminal sequence of the β-chains of normal adult human hemoglobin," *Jour. Am. Chem. Soc.,* **80,** 3358–3361.

————, ————, and PAULING, L., 1957. "A quantitative study of the hydrolysis of human dinitrophenyl(DNP)-globin: The number and kind of polypeptide chains in normal adult human hemoglobin," *Jour. Am. Chem. Soc.,* **79,** 4682–4686.

RUCKNAGEL, D. L., and NEEL, J. V., 1961. "The hemoglobinopathies." *Progress in Medical Genetics,* (Steinberg, A. G., ed.), New York: Grune and Stratton, I, 158–260.

SCHROEDER, W. A., 1960. Cited in Rucknagel and Neel, 1961.

————, and MATSUDA, G., 1958. "N-Terminal residues of human fetal hemoglobin," *Jour. Am. Chem. Soc.,* **80,** 1521.

SELA, M., WHITE, F. H., JR., and ANFINSEN, C. B., 1957. "Reductive cleavage of disulfide bridges in ribonuclease," *Science,* **125,** 691–692.

TSUGITA, A., GISH, D. T., YOUNG, J., FRAENKEL-CONRAT, H. KNIGHT, C. A., and STANLEY, W. M., 1960. "The complete amino acid sequence of the protein of tobacco mosaic virus," *Proc. Natl. Acad. Sci. U. S.,* **46,** 1463–1469.

VINOGRAD, J. R., HUTCHINSON, W. D., and SCHROEDER, W. A., 1959. "C^{14}-hybrids of human hemoglobins. II. The identification of the aberrant chain in human hemoglobin S," *Jour. Am. Chem. Soc.,* **81,** 3168–3169.

chapter four

Mechanisms for the Synthesis of Proteins

In the previous chapters we reviewed the function of DNA as the carrier of genetic information regulating the primary structure of proteins. Now we shall consider the means by which DNA exercises this control.

THE BIOSYNTHESIS OF PROTEINS

The detailed steps by which proteins are synthesized is one of the more difficult problems of biochemistry. It has been known for some years that RNA is involved in the process. For example, tissues with a high rate of protein synthesis, such as the silk gland of the silk worm, have a high RNA content. Conversely, tissues with a low rate of protein synthesis have a relatively low RNA content, even though these tissues may have very high metabolic activity.

Caspersson (1941) and Brachet (1942), working independently, each suggested that RNA plays a role in the synthesis of proteins. Their evidence was based on cytological studies, and, although the theory went considerably beyond the evidence, much of it has proved to be essentially correct. From their studies and from subsequent studies using radioactive tracers, it appears that RNA is the principal high molecular weight "messenger" that carries information from the nucleus to the cytoplasm. RNA is synthesized in the nucleus, afterward migrating into the cytoplasm. It does not migrate in detectable quantities in the reverse direction. Protein is synthesized in both the nucleus and the cytoplasm, but particularly in the latter. In bacterial systems it can be demonstrated that synthesis of protein is closely associated with RNA synthesis.

The modern era of studies in protein synthesis began in 1955 (Hoagland), with the preparation of a cell-free system that had the ability to incorporate labeled amino acids into newly synthesized protein. This mixture was found to consist of (1) large ribonucleoprotein particles found in the ribosomes (or microsomes), (2) small molecular weight RNA, sometimes designated soluble RNA or SRNA, (3) a series of activating enzymes, (4) adenosine triphosphate (ATP), and (5) amino acids.

The first step in protein synthesis, as shown in Fig. 4-1, is the activation of amino acids (Hoagland, *et al.*, 1956). This involves the reaction of the amino acid with ATP to yield the aminoacyl adenylate (a mixed anhydride) and pyrophosphate.

$$\text{Ad—R—PPP} + \text{AA} + \text{En} \longrightarrow \text{En·Ad—R—P—AA} + \text{PP}$$

Each of the enzymes that catalyze this reaction is specific for one amino acid. There are consequently twenty enzymes necessary for incorporation of all amino acids. The aminoacyl adenylate formed is not released into solution. Instead, it remains attached to the enzyme until it is transferred to SRNA (Zamecnik, *et al.*, 1958).

The SRNA consists of RNA molecules of molecular weight 30 to 50 thousand. There are known to be different SRNA molecules for each amino acid. For example, if an amino acid, ATP, the enzyme fraction, and SRNA are mixed together, the amino acid will be bound to SRNA until the SRNA is completely saturated. If a different amino acid is then added, it, too, will become bound until the SRNA is saturated with the second amino acid. The interpretation is that SRNA consists of a mixture of molecules, each specific for one amino acid. Saturation of the sites specific for glycine has no effect on alanine-binding sites.

The reaction itself consists in transferring the aminoacyl moiety to the terminal nucleotide of SRNA (Hecht, L. I., *et al.*, 1958). This nucleotide appears always to be adenylic acid, which in turn is connected to a sequence of two cytidylic acids. The structure of the SRNA is not known beyond that point. The amino acid forms an ester linkage with the 2'-(or 3'-)hydroxyl of the ribose of the terminal adenylate. The next step is much more obscure. It is thought that the amino acid-SRNA complexes align themselves on a large RNA template, the SRNA serving somehow as an adaptor that can

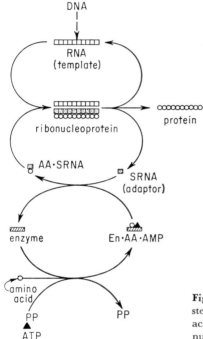

Fig. 4-1. Schematic representation of the steps involved in incorporation of amino acids into proteins. The nature of the ribonucleoprotein complex is largely unknown.

recognize the code on the template by a sort of complementariness. The amino acids are thus spatially arranged in a specific sequence so that they can form polypeptide chains with the proper composition. No enzyme has yet been isolated that carries out the function of forming peptide bonds. Formation of peptide bonds would break the covalent bonds binding the amino acids to RNA. This would permit the polypeptide chain to separate from its template and fold up into the proper tertiary structure. It is not known how much the proximity of the RNA influences the folding of the protein. It may promote folding to a specific configuration that might otherwise take a long time to achieve by thermal agitation.

THE CODING OF DNA

It has not been established that the DNA code for each amino acid is arranged in the same sequence on the DNA helix as the corresponding amino acids in the polypeptide chain. This is a most attractive hypothesis, however, and one that is being tested in several laboratories. On the assumption that some such relationship exists, attempts have been made to define the mathematical relationships that might characterize a code.

As stated earlier, the information for the amino acid sequences is no doubt contained in the sequence of base pairs of the DNA. There are 20 amino acids, however, and only four bases; so more than one base pair must be used for each amino acid. Two bases would yield only 16 possible combinations; therefore, at least three bases must be used. This gives a total of 64 combinations—which may be too many, depending on how the combinations are to be recognized. A so-called code with commas is a code in which each word (a word being the information necessary to specify one amino acid) is separated from the next word by a sign that indicates a space. This would presumably be a certain combination of bases. If a code with commas is used, then a lot of nonsense words would be possible.

Fig. 4-2. Illustration of a commaless code based on four letters with three letters per word. The code can be read only if one takes the proper three letters. Other "nonsense" words will not be in the "dictionary."

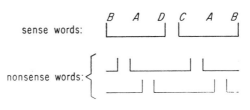

A code that has attracted much attention is the three-letter, commaless code of Crick, Griffith, and Orgel (1957). In this code only the nonoverlapping groups of three letters are sense words. To illustrate, there may be a sequence of letters as shown in Fig. 4-2. Two sense words are shown, with the nonsense words formed by placing these two words adjacent to each other. Since there are no known restrictions on the sequence of amino acids, it should be possible for either word to be repeated. The overlapping three-letter combinations would necessarily be nonsense words.

Crick, Griffith, and Orgel found that several such codes could be constructed with four letters taken three at a time. The interesting feature of their codes was that exactly 20 sense words could be formed in this way, the remaining combinations being nonsense words. Several other codes can be devised that also yield 20 sense combinations. Therefore, the mere fact of producing 20 sense words is not a strong argument in favor of a particular code. If codes based on more than three letters are used, then the considerations that have helped formulate the three-letter code become much less restrictive.

It should be possible to ascertain the number of bases required to specify an amino acid by estimating the number of amino acid residues under the control of a given segment of DNA. If it were possible to know the amino acid composition of all of the protein products of some microorganism, then it should be possible to measure the total DNA per cell and obtain a ratio of DNA to amino acids. There is as yet no organism for which all the protein products are known.

An alternate method would be to measure the number of amino acid residues in a single protein controlled by a recognized segment of DNA. This has been done by Levinthal (1960) for alkaline phosphatase in *E. coli*. He found that a chromosome segment that is approximately 0.2 map units long controls the synthesis of a protein unit of molecular weight 40,000. This segment of DNA in *E. coli* contains roughly 2000 base pairs. The basic protein unit is thought to contain 400 amino acids, giving a ratio of 5 base pairs per amino acid. This is not a reliable figure, because of experimental errors and assumptions. The true value may differ from 5 by 1 or 2 in either direction. The significance of the estimate lies in the confirmation of a code based on a small number of base pairs per amino acid.

One of the fascinating problems of the future will be to work out the actual code associated with each amino acid. It would be premature to predict the techniques that will provide the answer. In an earlier chapter it was suggested that mutational spectra, making use of specific mutagenic agents, may be of value. Some promise has also been obtained from chemical studies. There are no prospects for an immediate solution. It is generally assumed that the same code is used by all organisms, although there is no evidence for the assumption. The large variation in base composition of DNA in different species could reflect either differences in code or differences in noncoding parts of DNA.

QUANTITATIVE ASPECTS OF PROTEIN SYNTHESIS

A fertilized egg has the potential for synthesizing all the variety of proteins of a mature organism. There is evidence, however, that some proteins that will play an important role in the later life of the organism are not synthesized at this early stage. It also seems very likely that all nucleated cells in a fully differentiated organism contain the information for the synthesis of the vast array of proteins necessary for the many functions of the organism. Yet the various tissues of an organism do not produce the same proteins. It can be shown in some cases that cells have the potential for synthesizing proteins that they do not normally make. One of the better examples of this is found in enzyme induction.

Enzyme induction

One aspect of gene action that is justifiably receiving great attention has to do with the factors regulating the amounts of specific proteins synthesized by cells. It is not at all apparent why a cell having the potential to make a given protein may make none at all, or, at the other extreme, why a cell may make very little else. Between these extremes there are enzymes that may be made in varying amounts as needed to maintain the correct internal environment. Such changes in enzyme synthesis are frequently described as "adaptation," but this is merely attaching a label descriptive of the end result to an unknown process.

It is certain, though, that during the course of development various tissues follow characteristic patterns of protein synthesis, the amount and type of product depending on the state of differentiation and the site. This is illustrated in Fig. 4-3. To account for these differences, mechanisms for turning protein synthesis on and off must be introduced.

An enzyme that has been useful in the study of this phenomenon is β-galactosidase of *E. coli*. It continues to be a favorite for the study of regulatory mechanisms in protein synthesis. The enzyme itself catalyzes the hydrolysis of β-galactosides as indicated at the top of page 69.

A number of other groups can be substituted for the methyl group without changing the ability of the compound to serve as a substrate. *E. coli* does not usually produce the enzyme in the absence of galactosides. If a galactoside is added to the medium, the cells

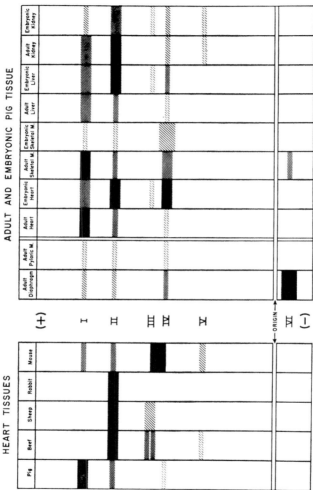

Fig. 4-3. The results of starch gel electrophoresis of various tissues and several species at different stages of development. The starch gels were stained to reveal enzymes with lactic dehydrogenase (LDH) activity. Electrophoresis reveals the great number of enzymes that may contribute to a given enzyme "activity." The various enzymes with common activity have been designated "isozymes." Although the total LDH activity may not vary dramatically during development, this diagram shows that the activity may be due to quite different enzymes. (From Markert and Møller, 1959.)

$$
\begin{array}{ccc}
\text{O--CH}_3 & & \text{OH} \\
\beta \mid & & \mid \\
\text{HC}\!\!-\!\!\rceil & & \text{HC}\!\!-\!\!\rceil \\
\mid & & \mid \\
\text{HO--CH} & & \text{HO--CH} \\
\mid & \xrightarrow[\text{H}_2\text{O}]{\beta\text{-galactosidase}} & \mid \\
\text{HO--CH}\quad\text{O} & & \text{HO--CH}\quad\text{O} \;+\; \text{CH}_3\text{OH} \\
\mid & & \mid \\
\text{HC--OH} & & \text{HC--OH} \\
\mid & & \mid \\
\text{HC}\!\!-\!\!\rfloor & & \text{HC}\!\!-\!\!\rfloor \\
\mid & & \mid \\
\text{CH}_2\text{OH} & & \text{CH}_2\text{OH}
\end{array}
$$

methyl-β-D-galactoside   D-galactose

immediately start producing large amounts of β-galactosidase. Thus, they appear to adapt to their environment, and the enzymes produced were earlier referred to as adaptive enzymes.

Monod (1956) demonstrated that such enzymes do not acquire their specificity from the environment. Using *E. coli*, he was able to separate the inducing function of galactosides from the substrate function. This is shown in Fig. 4-4. Since methyl-β-D-thiogalactoside, or thiomethylgalactoside (TMG), can serve as an inducer but not as a substrate, with the converse relationship for phenylgalactoside, it is obvious that the enzyme specificity is not conferred by the inducer. Hence it is preferable to speak of enzyme induction rather than adaptation. The enzyme owes its configuration entirely to the genetic constitution of the organism and not to the inducing substance. The latter serves only as a switch for turning on enzyme synthesis.

In addition to the strains of *E. coli* that are inducible for β-galactosidase, there are related strains that synthesize the enzyme whether or not the inducer is present. The enzyme in such strains is said to be constitutive. Constitutive strains can arise from inducible strains by mutation. The existence of these two types of cells permits some insight into the mechanism of enzyme induction. It is possible either that the constitutive strain synthesizes its own inducer internally and hence is in a constant state of "induction," or that the inducible strain is in a constant state of "repression" because of some type of repressor molecules that are inhibited by inducer substances and that are lacking in constitutive strains. In other

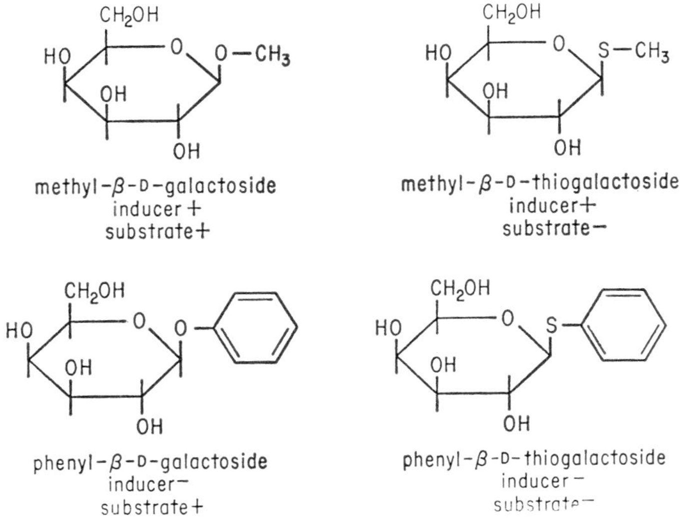

Fig. 4-4. Separation of the induction and substrate function for β-galactosidase in *E. coli*. (From Monod, 1956.)

words, does a constitutive strain have built-in inducer, or does the inducible strain have built-in repressor?

An answer has been obtained in the case of galactosidase in *E. coli* (Pardee, Jacob, and Monod, 1959). In this organism the ability to synthesize the enzyme is controlled by a locus designated z. Cells of genotype z^+ have the potential for synthesizing galactosidase; z^- cells have lost this potential by mutation. Adjacent to the z locus, but in a different cistron, is the i locus, which controls the inducibility of galactosidase. "Wild-type" i^+ cells are inducible; i^- mutants are constitutive. During mating the bacterial chromosome is transferred through a small cytoplasmic bridge from the male to the female cells. If an i^+z^+ chromosome is transferred into an i^-z^- cell in the absence of external inducer, two possible outcomes could be predicted, depending on the mechanism of inducibility. (1) If the recipient cell, which is constitutive (i^-) but which cannot make normal enzyme (z^-), has internal inducer already present, then the introduced z^+ should begin to make enzyme as soon as it enters the i^- cytoplasm. (2) If the recipient cell has lost the ability to repress enzyme synthesis (an ability retained by the introduced i^+ gene), then enzyme synthesis should occur only to the point where the $i+$ gene has had the opportunity to build up levels of repressor.

Experimentally the results conform to the second hypothesis. This is interpreted to mean that synthesis of inducible enzymes is normally repressed, and that the function of inducer molecules is to overcome repression.

The significance of this experiment for theories of regulation of protein synthesis cannot be overemphasized. For example, in cases where the production of repressors is also under genetic control, an interference in function of repressor synthesis, such as mutation, would result in increased synthesis of enzyme. On the other hand, interference with an inducer system would result in decreased enzyme. The nature of the repressor substances is unknown. As we shall see in the next section, small molecules can repress the synthesis of enzymes, forming negative feedback systems. (Negative feedback, a term used originally in engineering, means that the product of a reaction can inhibit its own synthesis.) In the case of β-galactosidase the repressor appears to be controlled by a single genetic locus. Furthermore, the formation of repressor molecules does not appear to require protein synthesis. This suggests the possibility that the repressor is a direct gene product rather than a small metabolite. Such a product might consist of RNA that has the ability to form relatively stable complexes either with the protein-RNA template during protein synthesis, or with the substrate (or other inducer). A diagram of this mechanism is shown in Fig. 4-5. The diagram includes much that is speculation and that will doubtless undergo many changes and amplifications as experimental evidence becomes available.

The importance for man of released enzyme synthesis has still to be ascertained. It would seem likely to play a large role in differentiation. The most thoroughly studied case of induction clearly demonstrated in man and other higher mammals is that of tryptophan peroxidase (Knox and Mehler, 1951). This enzyme, responsible for the opening of the indole ring of tryptophan to form formylkynurenine, is present only in trace amounts prior to birth. Shortly after birth the enzyme increases to levels characteristic of infancy. By administering large amounts of tryptophan, it is possible to increase the amount of tryptophan peroxidase in the liver about twofold. This represents *de novo* synthesis of protein and not merely enzyme activation. On the basis of the repressor hypothesis, a repressor would be present prior to birth that could

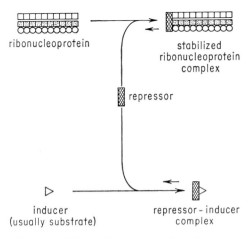

Fig. 4-5. Schematic representation of one way in which a repressor might work. The inducer removes the repressor by mass action, thus permitting the template-protein complex to dissociate. The diagram is not intended to represent actual mechanism.

not be overcome by the amount of tryptophan present at that time. Subsequent to birth the amount of tryptophan becomes adequate to overcome the repressor.

The repressor hypothesis is also interesting in the interpretation of various metabolic diseases involving pathways associated with phenylalanine or tryptophan. It has been pointed out that several enzymes, such as tryptophan peroxidase and phenylalanine hydroxylase, increase at the time of birth, suggesting that an inducer acts at that time. If for some reason the inducer failed to work, then the enzyme might fail to form, even though there would be no defect per se in the enzyme synthesizing mechanism. Thus, the cause of certain diseases in which there is a lack of a specific enzyme might be traced to a defect or absence of inducer (Nemeth and Nachmias, 1958). But if the phenomenon of induction depends instead on a repressor, then the failure of an enzyme to form is not likely to be due to a defect apart from the enzyme itself or the transport mechanisms that bring substrate into the cell.

It would be premature to conclude that only one method of induction or release exists. Only the principle of penury favors a single mechanism at present. Developments in this area of bio-chemical genetics will surely provide interesting material in the next few years.

Feedback repression

In addition to enzyme induction, which is primarily associated with the ability of a cell to handle substances from its environment, there are also regulatory mechanisms—negative feedback—associated with products of biosynthetic pathways. This type of repression is observed when the product of a metabolic pathway represses the synthesis of the enzymes responsible for its formation. Examples of this type of repression have been observed for several substances.

An interesting example is found in the studies reported by Ames and Garry (1959) on histidine biosynthesis in *Salmonella typhimurium*. The metabolic steps leading to histidine are shown in Fig. 4-6. The chromosomal locations of the mutations responsible for deficiencies in the various enzymes have been established and are shown in Fig. 4-7. Ames and Garry studied the effect of different levels of exogenous histidine on the last four enzymes of the path-way B to D. They found that the addition of large amounts of histidine to the medium suppressed the synthesis of all four enzymes. In contrast, when histidine was present in low levels, the enzymes were readily synthesized so that the cells did not lack histidine. The enzymes can be separated on a cellulose column, which indi-cates that the results are not due to a single molecule with multiple specificities.

The values of a feedback mechanism of this type are obvious. It prevents the synthesis of excessive amounts of end product, which might upset the balance among biochemical reactions. Furthermore, it prevents the wasteful synthesis of unnecessary protein. How wide-spread feedback repression is has not been established. It would seem, from the number of examples recently described, that feedback may be a major means of achieving metabolic regulation.

Variations in template efficiency

A source of quantitative variation of protein synthesis that is still only theoretical is the efficiency with which proteins are made by a template. This might happen in either of two ways. In the first there would be an amino acid substitution in the protein product, resulting in a change in the readiness with which the

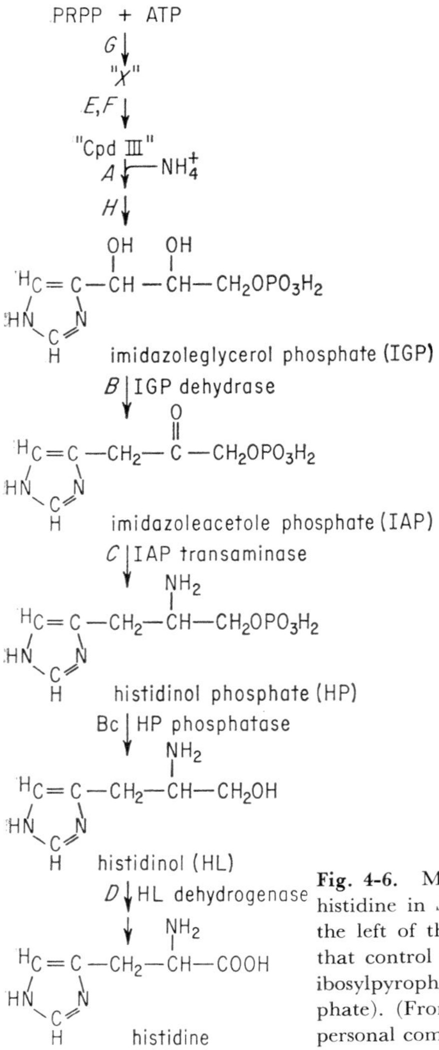

PRPP + ATP

$G \downarrow$

"χ"

$E,F \downarrow$

"Cpd III"

$A \downarrow \!\!\!\!-NH_4^+$

$H \downarrow$

$$\underset{\underset{\overset{|}{C}}{HN}\diagdown\diagup N}{H_C = C} - \overset{\overset{OH}{|}}{CH} - \overset{\overset{OH}{|}}{CH} - CH_2OPO_3H_2$$

imidazoleglycerol phosphate (IGP)

$B \mid$ IGP dehydrase

$$\underset{\underset{\overset{|}{C}}{HN}\diagdown\diagup N}{H_C = C} - CH_2 - \overset{\overset{O}{\parallel}}{C} - CH_2OPO_3H_2$$

imidazoleacetole phosphate (IAP)

$C \mid$ IAP transaminase

$$\underset{\underset{\overset{|}{C}}{HN}\diagdown\diagup N}{H_C = C} - CH_2 - \overset{\overset{NH_2}{|}}{CH} - CH_2OPO_3H_2$$

histidinol phosphate (HP)

$Bc \mid$ HP phosphatase

$$\underset{\underset{\overset{|}{C}}{HN}\diagdown\diagup N}{H_C = C} - CH_2 - \overset{\overset{NH_2}{|}}{CH} - CH_2OH$$

histidinol (HL)

$D \downarrow$ HL dehydrogenase

$$\underset{\underset{\overset{|}{C}}{HN}\diagdown\diagup N}{H_C = C} - CH_2 - \overset{\overset{NH_2}{|}}{CH} - COOH$$

histidine

Fig. 4-6. Metabolic pathway for biosynthesis of histidine in *Salmonella typhimurium*. The letters to the left of the arrows designate the genetic loci that control these reactions (PRPP = phosphoribosylpyrophosphate, ATP = adenosine triphosphate). (From Hartman, *et al.*, 1960; Hartman, personal communication.)

protein could form or dissociate from the RNA template. Such a change in protein structure might or might not affect the functioning of the protein. In the second mechanism there would be a change in the RNA template at a point not involved in the amino acid sequence of the product but again involved in the rate at which the polypeptide chain is formed or dissociated. The protein thus produced would be normal; the rate at which it is produced would be sometimes faster but probably more often slower.

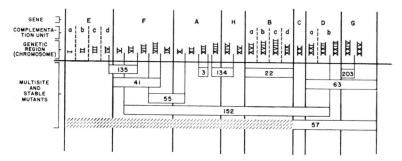

Fig. 4-7. Linkage map of histidine mutants in *Salmonella typhimurium*. The chromosomal alignment of genes in the same sequence in which the enzymes function metabolically is a very interesting feature observed in several organisms. However, many exceptions are known and this arrangement does not appear to be universally advantageous to organisms. (From Hartman, *et al.*, 1960.)

Technical difficulties have made it impossible to identify variations in protein synthesis with variations in template efficiency. A probable example of a change in template efficiency is found in the abnormal hemoglobins (Neel, 1959). Hemoglobin S comprises only 20 to 40 percent of the total hemoglobin in a person heterozygous for this gene, the exact level being somewhat characteristic of an individual. The S allele is therefore less efficient in producing its product, although efficiency in this case has not been specifically associated with a template process. Some of the abnormal hemoglobins may be abnormal only because they cannot be produced fast enough to avoid anemia. Indeed, interference with the oxygen transport function is observed in only a few abnormal hemoglobins. Other examples of variations in template efficiency may include the thalassemias (Ingram and Stretton, 1959).

Variations in number of ribosomes

A final way in which the amount of protein synthesized might be varied is by a change in the number of ribosomes. It is not known how many ribosomes with the same function are present in a cell. In certain secretory cells, there must be a great many. The technical problem of studying function of individual ribosomes has not been solved.

There are two examples in man showing variations in the number of protein synthesizing "machines." These are the carrier states of galactosemia (Hsia, *et al.,* 1958; Kirkman and Bynum, 1959; Bretthauer, *et al.,* 1959) and acatalasemia (Nishimura, *et al.,* 1959). In both cases it has been possible to do direct enzyme assays on appropriate cells (erythrocytes), with the finding that individuals heterozygous for these genes have on the average about half the normal amount of enzyme. Since the functional enzyme present originates from the one normal gene, it seems inescapable that only half the usual number of normal ribosomes is present. In the examples cited, it is not certain that the mutant genes are not represented by ribosomes unable to function or by ribosomes whose product is devoid of enzyme activity. It is even possible that such nonfunctioning ribosomes might be counted by regulating mechanisms that control the number of ribosomes representing a given genetic locus.

In the examples cited there is a 1:1 relation between the number of functional genes and the amount of protein synthesized. These systems would seem to be free from the feedback mechanisms discussed in previous paragraphs. There may be some systems, however, in which the number of ribosomes is influenced by conditions within the cell.

LITERATURE CITED

Ames, B. N., and Garry, B., 1959. "Coordinate repression of the synthesis of four histidine biosynthetic enzymes by histidine," *Proc. Natl. Acad. Sci. U. S.,* **45,** 1453–1461.

Brachet, J., 1942. "La localisation des acides pentosenucléiques dans les tissus animaux et les oeufs d'Amphibiens en voie de développement," *Arch. Biol.* (Liege), **53,** 207–257.

Bretthauer, R. K., Hansen, R. G., Donnell, G., and Bergren, W. R., 1959. "A procedure for detecting carriers of galactosemia," *Proc. Natl. Acad. Sci. U. S.,* **45,** 328.

Caspersson, T., 1941. "Studien über den Eiweissumsatz der Zelle," *Naturwissenschaften,* **29,** 33–43.

Crick, F. H. C., Griffith, J. S., and Orgel, L. E., 1957. "Codes without commas," *Proc. Natl. Acad. Sci. U. S.,* **43,** 416–421.

HARTMAN, P. E., LOPER, J. C., and SERMAN, D., 1960. "Fine structure mapping by complete transduction between histidine-requiring *Salmonella* mutants," *Jour. Gen. Microbiol.*, **22**, 323–353.

HECHT, L. I., ZAMECNIK, P. C., STEPHENSON, M. L., and SCOTT, J. F., 1958. "Nucleoside triphosphates as precursors of ribonucleic acid end groups in a mammalian system," *Jour. Biol. Chem.*, **233**, 954–963.

HOAGLAND, M. B., 1955. "An enzymic mechanism for amino acid activation in animal tissues," *Biochim. et Biophys. Acta*, **16**, 288–289.

———, KELLER, E. B., and ZAMECNIK, P. C., 1956. "Enzymatic carboxyl activation of amino acids," *Jour. Biol. Chem.*, **218**, 345–358.

HSIA, D. Y.-Y., HUANG, I., and DRISCOLL, S. G., 1958. "The heterozygous carrier in galactosaemia," *Nature*, **182**, 1389–1390.

INGRAM, V. M., and STRETTON, A. O. W., 1959. "Genetic basis of the thalassaemia diseases," *Nature*, **184**, 1903–1909.

KIRKMAN, H. N., and BYNUM, E., 1959. "Enzymic evidence of a galactosemic trait in parents of galactosemic children," *Ann. Human Genetics*, **23**, 117.

KNOX, W. E., and MEHLER, A. H., 1951. "The adaptive increase of the tryptophan peroxidase-oxidase system of liver," *Science*, **113**, 237–238.

LEVINTHAL, C., 1960. In *First Conference on Genetics* (Sutton, H. E., ed.), New York: Josiah Macy, Jr. Foundation, pp. 102–105.

MARKERT, C. L., and MØLLER, F., 1959. "Multiple forms of enzymes: tissue, ontogenetic, and species specific patterns," *Proc. Natl. Acad. Sci. U. S.*, **45**, 753–763.

MONOD, J., 1956. "Remarks on the mechanism of enzyme induction," in *Enzymes: Units of Biological Structure and Function* (Gaebler, O. H., ed.), New York: Academic Press, pp. 7–28.

NEEL, J. V., 1959. "Aspects of the genetic control of the structure of the hemoglobin molecule," *Proc. X Internat. Cong. Genetics*, Vol. I, Toronto: Univ. of Toronto Press, pp. 108–119.

NEMETH, A. M., and NACHMIAS, V. T., 1958. "Changes in tryptophan peroxidase activity in developing liver," *Science*, **128**, 1085–1086.

NISHIMURA, E. T., HAMILTON, H. B., KOBARA, T. Y., TAKAHARA, S., OGURA, Y., and DOI, K., 1959. "Carrier state in human acatalasemia," *Science*, **130**, 333–334.

PARDEE, A. B., JACOB, F., and MONOD, J., 1959. "The genetic control and cytoplasmic expression of 'inducibility' in the synthesis of β-galactosidase by *E. coli*," *Jour. Mol. Biol.*, **1**, 165–178.

ZAMECNIK, P. C., STEPHENSON, M. L., and HECHT, L. I., 1958. "Intermediate reactions in amino acid incorporation," *Proc. Natl. Acad. Sci. U. S.*, **44**, 73–78.

chapter five ➤➤➤➤ Errors of
Metabolism

All known inherited defects of metabolism can be ascribed
either to a defective protein, usually an enzyme, or to a defect in
the mechanisms for regulating protein synthesis. In the previous
chapter some of the main features of protein synthesis and regulation were outlined. We shall now consider some of the ways in which
defects in protein function may give rise to aberrations in metabolism and result in disease.

METABOLIC BLOCKS

Most known metabolic defects are of the "metabolic block"
variety. By a block is meant the loss of ability to catalyze some
essential reaction. Blocks can arise by a variety of mechanisms, but
a primary block probably always results from a loss of function of
a specific protein.

Primary blocks

Every protein synthesized by an organism presumably has some
specific essential function at some time during the life of the organism, or at least did have during the lives of recent ancestors. If a
mutation occurs resulting in no enzyme or in an enzyme that has
lost most of its catalytic ability, then a specific reaction will no
longer occur at the normal rate. This inability to function at a
normal capacity can be designated as a primary block in metabolism.

The consequences of a primary block will vary with the reaction studied. In general, if the block is in the conversion of substance A to B,

$$A \longrightarrow\!\!\mid\!\mid\!\rightarrow B$$

then A will accumulate and B will be found in decreased quantities. The absolute magnitude of these effects will depend on the sources of A and B and the other reactions in which they participate. If the sole source of B is A, then it may be completely lacking. On the other hand, if it can also arise through other mechanisms, then these may be able to compensate, at least in part, for the decreased formation of B from A. If A is supplied primarily from other metabolic pathways, then equilibria may be such that A does not accumulate to high levels. If the synthesis of A includes some irreversible reactions, then A will accumulate and either be excreted as such or be converted to products other than B. These other products may not be normal metabolites. If A is a dietary constituent, the degree of accumulation will depend on the nature of the diet.

The effects of a primary block again will depend on many factors. If the primary function of the blocked reaction is to furnish an essential compound B or some product of B, then the block may be deleterious if there is no alternate source of B. If the function of the reaction is to dispose of A, then the block may be relatively benign if A can be excreted without interfering with other reactions.

Although relatively few inherited diseases have been traced to primary metabolic blocks, those few provide examples for most of the possibilities outlined. One of the better known in man causes the disease phenylketonuria. Some of the normal pathways of phenylalanine metabolism are shown in Fig. 5-1. Phenylalanine is an essential amino acid that cannot be synthesized by higher mammals and must therefore be supplied in the diet. Its only known function is as a constituent of proteins. Since the body normally takes in much more than needed for protein synthesis, most of the phenylalanine is oxidized to tyrosine. The latter is a precursor for melanin pigments, thyroxine, and epinephrine, and is also a protein constituent. It is supplied in the diet and by oxidation of phenylalanine, and the excess is converted to p-hydroxyphenylpyruvate by transamination in the liver or under some circumstances perhaps by deamination in the kidney. This compound is further oxidized as indicated.

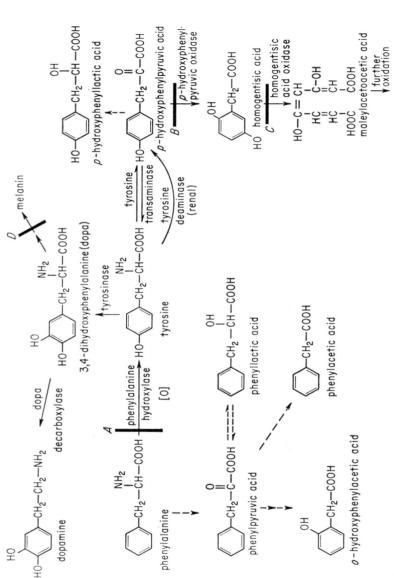

Fig. 5-1. Principal metabolic pathways of phenylalanine. Solid arrows are reactions that are important in normal metabolism. Broken arrows become quantitatively important in phenylketonuria. The solid bars indicate blocks in A, phenylketonuria; B, tyrosinosis; C, alkaptonuria; and D, albinism. Only A and C have been proved to be primary.

The conversion of phenylalanine to tyrosine is catalyzed by the enzyme phenylalanine hydroxylase. It is a rather labile enzyme and is found in detectable quantities only in liver. Individuals who are homozygous for the phenylketonuria gene lack the capacity to carry out of the oxidation of phenylalanine. This is due to primary absence of enzyme activity, as has been demonstrated by assay of liver samples from phenylketonuric patients (Mitoma, *et al.*, 1957; Wallace, *et al.*, 1957). Since the only normal pathway for phenylalanine oxidation is blocked, and since phenylalanine is efficiently reabsorbed by the renal tubules, the level of phenylalanine builds up in the blood and intracellular fluids. Instead of a normal blood phenylalanine level of 1 mg per 100 ml, phenylketonurics may have a level of 50 mg per 100 ml. As a consequence, reactions that are normally of little significance become very important. For example, phenylpyruvic acid is not a normal constituent of urine, and *o*-hydroxyphenylacetic acid occurs only in very low amounts. In phenylketonurics these two substances and phenylalanine are major excretory products.

Alkaptonurics are characterized by the excretion of homogentisic acid. This is a substance that oxidizes spontaneously when exposed to air, causing the urine to become black on standing. It is easily detected in infancy by the dark stains that form on diapers. Consequently it was one of the first inborn errors to be recognized. Feeding experiments suggested early that the block was in the oxidation of homogentisic acid, and recent studies of enzymes in livers of alkaptonuric patients indicate that active homogentisic acid oxidase is absent (La Du, *et al.*, 1958). In contrast to phenylalanine, homogentisic acid is not reabsorbed by the tubules; hence the blood levels remain very low. As a consequence, accessory metabolic pathways, if they exist, are not quantitatively important. The only consequence of this disease is a slow deposition of pigmented material in connective tissue, resulting in a relatively benign arthritic condition.

A third disease in which the primary block is known is galactosemia. Infants who are homozygous for the galactosemia gene are unable to utilize galactose, which is a constituent of lactose, the principal sugar found in milk. As a consequence the blood levels of galactose are greatly elevated and galactose is excreted in the urine. Other consequences are mental deficiency, cataracts, and aminoaciduria. Galactose is known to be utilized according to the equations of Fig. 5-2. It is possible to assay for the three enzymes shown in Fig. 5-2. In galactosemic individuals only galactose-1-phosphate uridyl transferase activity is missing (Anderson, *et al.*, 1957).

An interesting feature of galactose metabolism is that the same reactions are used by microorganisms to make galactose available

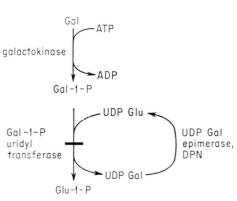

Fig. 5-2. Reactions for the conversion of galactose into glucose. After galactose is phosphorylated, an exchange reaction occurs with uridyldiphosphoglucose (UDPGlu), releasing glucose-1-phosphate and binding galactose to form UDPGal. By a reaction that probably involves oxidation and subsequent reduction, the configuration of the C^2-hydroxyl is changed to form UDPGlu. This can react with more galactose-1-phosphate in a cyclic fashion. All the reactions shown are reversible.

as a source of energy. There are a number of mutant forms of *E. coli* that cannot utilize galactose. These *gal⁻* stains have been studied for their specific enzyme deficiencies and have been found to be lacking either Gal-1-P-uridyl transferase or UDPGal epimerase (Kurahashi, 1957). Thus, some of the *gal⁻* mutants have the microbial equivalent of galactosemia. No inherited block associated with epimerase deficiency has yet been found in man.

Galactosemia provides an example of the importance of equilibria in determining the nature of the products that accumulate. Galactose-1-phosphate, a substrate for the blocked reaction, is of high energy content. Although it can be demonstrated to accumulate in various tissues—even in erythrocytes, which do not have a particularly active galactose pathway—the equilibrium of the galactokinase reaction favors free galactose, and this substance accounts for almost all the galactose moiety of the ingested lactose.

Secondary blocks

In many metabolic disorders the deleterious effects cannot be traced to deficiency in the product of the primary blocked reaction. In untreated phenylketonuria there is certainly no deficiency of tyrosine, which is readily available in the diet. Rather, the deleterious effects seem to result from a decreased activity of one or more reactions other than the one involving the primary block. These have sometimes been cited as evidence for the pleiotropic effects of a gene. As gene action is analyzed at the chemical level, however, it becomes apparent that true pleiotropism, or multiple gene action, probably does not exist. In cases where more than one effect can be observed, such as alteration in the activities of two or more enzymes, some of the effects can be shown to be secondary. All such multiple effects have thus far involved quantitative change in enzyme *activity*. A true test of pleiotropism would be the demonstration of qualitative changes in more than one protein. Such a possibility should not be denied, since it is possible that different proteins may make use of common polypeptide subunits, and a defective subunit would produce defects in all proteins that contain it. None of the cases that have been analyzed require this explanation, however.

A more common means of influencing reactions is by inhibition. The role of inhibition in regulatory mechanisms has already been discussed. The accumulation of metabolites above normal levels may result in inhibition of many reactions. If the inhibitors accumulate because of a primary block, then the enzymes on which they act may be described as being "secondarily blocked." A secondary block will rarely be complete. Instead, it will consist of reduced enzyme activity. Otherwise, the consequences of a secondary block are analogous to those of a primary block.

Examples of secondary blocks can be found in the diseases already discussed. In galactosemia the clinical symptoms of cataract, mental deficiency, and aminoaciduria involve reactions that have not been identified. These pathological consequences are thought to be the result of accumulation of galactose-1-phosphate in a variety of tissues. The galactose-1-phosphate probably acts as an inhibitor of reactions involving its analog, glucose-1-phosphate. Removal of galactose from the diet results in an absence of galactose-1-phosphate, and the inhibited reactions can then function normally.

The role of inhibition in phenylketonuria is even more readily demonstrated, because some of the inhibited reactions are known. In addition to alterations in excretion of phenyl derivatives, there is alteration of several indoles. Here, again, it was suggested that pleiotropism might explain these defects in two areas of metabolism; but the variations in indole metabolism have now been shown to be

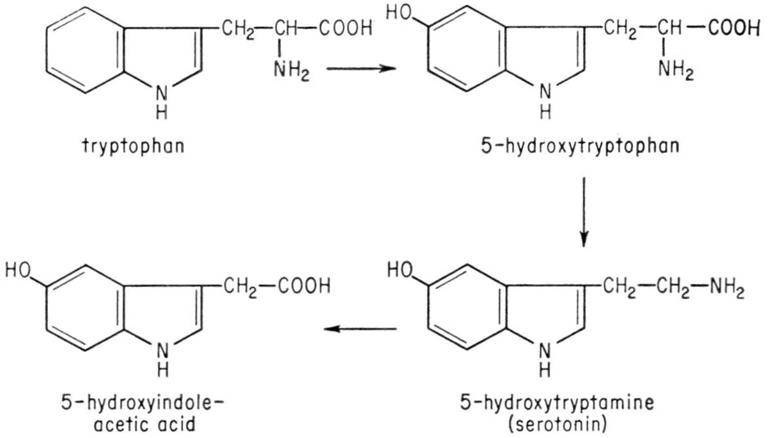

tryptophan

5-hydroxytryptophan

5-hydroxyindole-acetic acid

5-hydroxytryptamine (serotonin)

Fig. 5-3. The normal pathway of metabolism of tryptophan to 5-hydroxyindoleacetic acid.

entirely secondary. For example, it has been observed that the excretion of 5-hydroxyindoleacetic acid (5HIAA) is abnormally low in phenylketonurics. This substance is a metabolite of serotonin and is formed by the sequence of reactions shown in Fig. 5-3. The level of 5HIAA in urine is a useful indicator of the amount of tryptophan converted into serotonin, since virtually all serotonin is eventually excreted as 5HIAA and other sources are not known to contribute appreciably to the 5HIAA formed. The high levels of phenylalanine, or, more probably, one of its metabolites, inhibit some step in this pathway, resulting in decreased production of the end product. A dramatic reversal of the inhibition is seen if phenylalanine is removed from the diet (Fig. 5-4), showing that the blocked enzyme is present in normal levels.

Because some of the products that accumulate in phenylketonuria can be readily identified, it has been possible to study the effects of these compounds on various enzyme systems *in vitro*. Of the enzymes that have been given special attention, the most interesting are the amino acid decarboxylases, which use pyridoxal phosphate as a coenzyme. These include 5-hydroxytryptophan decarboxylase, tryptophan decarboxylase, dopa decarboxylase and glutamic acid decarboxylase. These L-amino acid decarboxylases all give

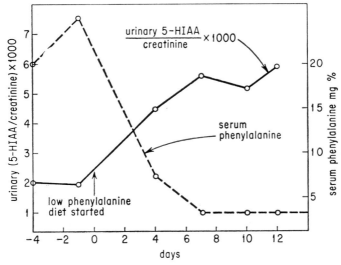

Fig. 5-4. The effect of removal of phenylalanine from the diet on excretion of 5-hydroxyindoleacetic acid by a phenylketonuric. (From Baldridge, *et al.*, 1959.)

rise to primary amines, which appear to be important to normal neurological function. Interference with decarboxylase activity might be responsible for the mental defect that is almost universally associated with phenylketonuria.

The effect of some aromatic compounds on decarboxylase activity is shown in Table 7, below. Phenylalanine itself is seen not to be an effective inhibitor. Some of the other compounds are quite effective. Since pyridoxine contains an aromatic ring, it has been suggested that the inhibitors compete with pyridoxal phosphate for an enzyme site. Pyridoxal phosphate does not reverse the inhibition, however, and recent studies suggest that the inhibitors compete with substrate (Hansen, 1959; Tashian, 1960).

The results shown in Table 7 illustrate the difficulty in extrapolating from *in vitro* to *in vivo* systems. An effective inhibitor of decarboxylase is *p*-hydroxyphenylacetic acid. This compound is a constituent of normal urine, occurring frequently at levels in the same order of magnitude as the abnormal metabolites of phenylketonuria; yet its inhibitory activity does not appear to affect

Table 7

Inhibition of Decarboxylase Activity by Aromatic Compounds Related to Phenylalanine. (From Sutton and Tashian, 1960.)

Compound	Dopa decarboxylase	5-Hydroxy-tryptophan decarboxylase	Glutamic acid decarboxylase
Phenylalanine	−	−	−
Phenylpyruvic acid	+, ++	++	+
Phenyllactic acid	−, ++	+	−
Phenylacetic acid	−, +	++	+, ++
p-Hydroxyphenylpyruvic acid	+		+
p-Hydroxyphenyllactic acid	+		
p-Hydroxyphenylacetic acid			+, ++
o-Hydroxyphenylacetic acid			+

++ strong inhibition; + moderate inhibition; − little or no inhibition.

adversely the individuals in whom it occurs. It might be concluded, therefore, that inhibition of decarboxylases is not an important feature of the pathology of phenylketonuria. It must be remembered, however, that inhibition can occur only if the enzyme and the inhibitor have an opportunity to come into contact. A substance formed by renal enzymes and promptly excreted can hardly enter into the metabolic picture of the organism. The same substance formed in the liver will have much greater effect. And if the substance were formed within nervous tissue, the effect would be even greater on the nervous system. In addition to differences in the sites of formation, there are also differences in transport mechanisms that may permit one compound to be concentrated by a tissue while a related compound is excluded. In fact, many effects may be invoked to account for differences between *in vitro* and *in vivo* action. It is probably best to say that *in vitro* action is a necessary condition of *in vivo* action, but not vice versa. If the two actions do correlate, the *in vitro* results may be relevant to the *in vivo* results. If a variety of compounds can inhibit to a greater or lesser degree the same array of reactions, and if these secondary blocks are responsible for the malfunctions we recognize as disease, then a particular syndrome will not necessarily be associated only with one primary block. No good example of this nonspecificity of etiology is known, but several possibilities have been suggested. There are children who have an array of defects similar to phenylketonurics without having a block in phenylalanine metabolism. Conceivably, such patients might have a block at some other point in aromatic metabolism resulting in less obvious urinary changes but inhibiting the same enzymes of the nervous system.

Bickel (1960) has suggested that the so-called Fanconi's renal rickets may be another example. The association of generalized aminoaciduria, glycosuria, and vitamin-D-resistant "rickets" is found both as a separate inherited entity and as an accompanying feature of several other diseases. The chemical changes that cause these abnormalities are not known. Bickel speculates that the same change may occur in all diseases with these symptoms and that this change is secondary to a variety of primary changes. Thus, Fanconi's renal rickets has been observed in cystine storage disease, in glycogen storage disease, and in Wilson's disease. This shows that a variety of genetic defects may result in a syndrome that, because of its uniformity, suggests the presence of a single genetic entity.

This idea is certainly not new in classical genetics. Many inherited traits are known to result from any of a number of genes at different loci. It is generally supposed that these genes are somehow related in their primary effects. This need not be true, since observations, more often than not, are limited to manifestations several steps removed from primary effects.

METABOLIC ACCELERATION

Just as mutations give rise to proteins that have lost their catalytic activity, so they may also give rise to proteins that have lost the ability to be inhibited by specific end products. These proteins would then no longer be regulated by feedback mechanisms designed to maintain metabolic balance. No case has yet been analyzed that is known to be a result of metabolic acceleration of this type. Such mutations are probably much rarer than metabolic blocks. Moreover, an accelerated reaction is undoubtedly more difficult to pinpoint than a block.

One disease in man that may result from inherited metabolic acceleration is hyperuricemia. Sometimes a high blood level of uric acid occurs without the appearance of clinical defect; sometimes it is associated with gout. In many families, hyperuricemia is inherited as a simple dominant, with higher levels of uric acid found in men than in women. To what extent other genes may influence the expression of the "principal hyperuricemia gene" has not been ascertained.

A principal defect in hyperuricemia seems to be the overproduction of uric acid, but the mechanism for overproduction has not been firmly established. Wyngaarden (1960) has suggested that overproduction may be due to a failure of the mechanisms that regulate the first step in the biosynthetic pathway of purines. This step is

α-phosphoribosylpyrophosphate (PRPP) + glutamine + H_2O

$\xrightarrow[\text{amidotransferase}]{\text{PRPP}}$ β-phosphoribosylamine + glutamic acid + pyrophosphate

A number of purines have been found to be competitive inhibitors of PRPP in this reaction, the most active being adenosine triphosphate and adenosine diphosphate (Wyngaarden and Ashton, 1959). These purine products of the pathway might function as regulators of the reaction, slowing it down as purine levels rise. If the enzyme PRPP amidotransferase were to become altered so that the end products no longer effectively inhibit it, then excessive synthesis would result. The excess purines would be metabolized to uric acid, causing the blood levels to increase.

There are still many observations that must be integrated into such a theory for hyperuricemia. Moreover, it is possible to devise schemes for overproduction of uric acid that are not based on a defective feedback mechanism (Wyngaarden, 1960). Whether or not this hypothesis for the defect in hyperuricemia can be confirmed, however, the principle of defective feedback systems would seem to be a mechanism that must be considered in metabolic diseases.

LITERATURE CITED

ANDERSON, E. P., KALCKAR, H. M., and ISSELBACHER, K. J., 1957. "Defect in uptake of galactose-1-phosphate into liver nucleotides in congenital galactosemia," *Science*, **125**, 113–114.

BALDRIDGE, R. C., BOROFSKY, L., BAIRD, H. III, REICHLE, F., and BULLOCK, D., 1959. "Relationships of serum phenylalanine levels and ability of phenylketonurics to hydroxylate tryptophan," *Proc. Soc. Expt. Biol. Med.*, **100**, 529–531.

BICKEL, H., 1960. "Die nicht-diabetischen Melliturien des Kindes," *Modern Problems in Pediatrics, Vol. 6*, (Hotlinger, A., and Berger, H., eds.) (*Bibliotheca Paediatrica*, no. 74), Basel: S. Karger, pp. 313–336.

HANSEN, A., 1959. "Action of phenylalanine metabolites on glutamic acid decarboxylase and γ-aminobutyric acid—α-ketoglutaric acid transaminase in brain," *Acta Chem. Scand.*, **13**, 1366.

KURAHASHI, K., 1957. "Enzyme formation in galactose-negative mutants of *Escherichia coli*," *Science*, **125**, 114–116.

LA DU B. N., ZANNONI, V. G., LASTER, L., and SEEGMILLER, J. E., 1958. "The nature of the defect in tyrosine metabolism in alcaptonuria," *Jour. Biol. Chem.*, **230**, 251.

MITOMA, C., AULD, R. M., and UDENFRIEND, S., 1957. "On the nature of the enzymatic defect in phenylpyruvic oligophrenia," *Proc. Soc. Expt. Biol. Med.*, **94**, 632.

SUTTON, H. E., and TASHIA, R. E., 1960. "Inherited variations in aromatic metabolism," *Metabolism*, **9**, 284–292.

TASHIAN, R. E., 1960. Unpublished results.

WALLACE, H. W., MOLDAVE, K., and MEISTER, A., 1957. "Studies on conversion of phenylalanine to tyrosine in phenylpyruvic oligophrenia," *Proc. Soc. Expt. Biol. Med.*, **94**, 632.

WYNGAARDEN, J. B., 1960. "Gout," in Stanbury, J. B., Wyngaarden, J. B., and Frederickson, D. S. (eds.) *The Metabolic Bases of Inherited Diseases*, New York: McGraw-Hill, pp. 679–760.

———, and ASHTON, D. M., 1959. "Feedback control of purine biosynthesis by purine ribonucleotides," *Nature*, **183**, 747–748.

chapter six

Hidden Genetic Variation; Detection of Genetic Carriers

Two interesting problems having to do with detection of hidden genetic variation have arisen in recent years. The more recent concerns "modern diseases," which are expressed as sensitivity to drugs. The other concerns the detection of individuals who are carriers of deleterious recessive genes. With increased availability of sensitive chemical methods, a number of carrier states can now be recognized.

VARIATION IN METABOLISM OF DRUGS

Three outstanding examples of differences in the capacity to handle drugs have been described with respect to genetic and metabolic mechanisms. Their interest lies in the fact that the circumstances under which the unusual responses were first detected are not likely ever to have arisen before the advent of modern medication. The variation is widespread geographically, and in some cases it must be assumed that selective factors favor heterozygous individuals, at least in certain environments.

Glucose-6-phosphate dehydrogenase deficiency

During World War II it was found that the antimalarial primaquine can precipitate hemolytic crises in a small percentage of subjects treated with it. In others it has no such effect. Since then primaquine sensitivity has been studied extensively and has been traced to a deficiency of glucose-6-phosphate dehydrogenase in erythrocytes (Carson, et al., 1956). The oxidation of glucose by this enzyme is a major source of reduced triphosphopyridine nucleotide (TPNH). The other source is the next reaction in that sequence, the oxidation of 6-phosphogluconate. TPNH is essential for the maintenance of reduced glutathione, which, in turn, is necessary to prevent deleterious effects of various foreign agents in the erythrocyte. Young cells have sufficient glucose-6-phosphate dehydrogenase to maintain protective levels of reduced glutathione. The enzyme is relatively unstable in sensitive individuals and older cells do not have enough of it to cope with the challenge of primaquine. It has not yet been possible to prove that the primary defect is in the structure of glucose-6-phosphate dehydrogenase. Most of the pathological effects can be traced to deficiency of this enzyme, however.

It eventually became apparent that individuals sensitive to primaquine are also sensitive to several other substances. Prominent among them is naphthalene, and the severe reaction to mothballs observed in some children is caused by this defect. The same defect has been implicated in favism, a hemolytic disease common in some Mediterranean areas. Favism occurs after consumption of fava beans (Vicia faba), particularly if they are eaten raw, as may happen among children. The toxic component of the beans has not been identified.

Evidence that the defect is hereditary was provided by the observation that sensitivity to primaquine is virtually limited to persons of certain racial groups. The trait was initially discovered among Negroes, about 10 percent of males being affected. It is also found among Sephardic Jews but not among Ashkenazic Jews in Israel. It is not generally found among other Caucasians, although some populations of Greece and Italy have it. Analysis of family data indicates that a gene on the X chromosome determines sensitivity. Thus, hemizygous males are sensitive. There are three classes of females: homozygous normal, homozygous sensitive, and heterozygous. There is much phenotypic overlap among the three groups, however, and it is not always possible to classify females accurately (Childs and Zinkham, 1959).

Attempts have been made to explain the high incidence of glucose-6-phosphate dehydrogenase deficiency by the relative advantage that sensitive individuals have in malarial areas. According to this theory, those affected would be less able to support parasites and therefore better able to survive, as in the case of sickle cell trait. Whether or not malaria proves to be an important factor, the theory emphasizes the point that a gene capable of causing a disease under one set of circumstances (primaquine administration) may be beneficial under others.

Serum cholinesterase types

An inherited trait less well studied genetically but very interesting chemically is manifested by a great reduction in the ability to hydrolyze certain esters of choline (Kalow, 1959). The trait was first detected when a few patients showed prolonged effects of the muscle relaxant succinylcholine. Further investigation showed that the serum cholinesterase (pseudocholinesterase) of these patients is abnormal. The Michaelis constant is much higher, indicating a much lower affinity of the enzyme for substrate. The lower affinity also extends to certain cholinesterase inhibitors.

Three types of individuals have been found: those with only the typical cholinesterase, those with only abnormal enzyme, and those with a mixture of the two. These correspond to the two homozygotes and the heterozygote. The gene frequency of the atypical gene is .02 among Caucasians. Atypical cholinesterase has not been associated with any naturally occurring diseases.

Isoniazid inactivation

Very little is known about this trait. Isoniazid is a drug used in the treatment of tuberculosis. It is metabolized ("inactivated") in the body, but two types of individuals have been detected, slow inactivators and rapid inactivators. The enzymic basis for the difference is unknown. Analysis of pedigrees indicates that rapid inactivation is transmitted as a simple autosomal dominant (Harris, et al., 1959). Here is another example of genetic variation in response to a drug that cannot have played a role in the biological history of man.

DETECTION OF GENETIC CARRIERS

If it were possible to identify all the individuals heterozygous for a recessively inherited trait, it should be possible, by avoiding matings between two such individuals, to prevent the occurrence of diseased offspring. When the trait is a severe disease, many people would be willing to accept restriction in their choice of a mate, even though three quarters of their offspring should escape the disease on the basis of probability. Normal siblings of affected individuals, with their close contact with the disease, are particularly concerned over the prospect of transmitting disease to their children. Since one third of the siblings of affected individuals are homozygous normal, it is very important to them to know their genetic status.

In addition to carriers of recessive genes there are also persons who may have the genetic constitution for disease but who do not develop it, either because of the presence of other genes or because of environmental factors. In such individuals the genes are said to be nonpenetrant, but such genes may be transmitted to offspring nevertheless. Penetrance may involve either a homozygous recessive gene or a heterozygous dominant gene. Although individuals in whom deleterious genes have failed to find expression cannot be classed strictly with carriers, the need to recognize them and the techniques for recognizing them are related.

A third objective of recognizing the presence of unexpressed genes, and this is related to the second, is to anticipate individuals who may later develop disease. There are many inherited diseases whose effects appear only in later life. An outstanding example is Huntington's chorea, a disease of the nervous system resulting from a dominant gene. The first signs of this disease commonly appear when the affected individual is in his twenties or thirties, although, rarely, persons with the gene do not manifest its effects until their sixties (Reed, et al., 1958). Recognition of affected individuals prior to the age of reproduction could greatly reduce the incidence of the disease. In some instances, if the condition is recognized in time, a person with an inherited potential for expressing a disease may be prevented from so doing by manipulation of the environment.

It is therefore of great concern to the geneticist to be able to recognize the presence of deleterious genes in a normal person. In order for such genes to be detected directly it is essential that they show some functional difference from the normal genes. Ordinarily this difference consists in a decrease in the primary gene product. This may or may not lead to changes that can be measured. In discussing the detection of carriers we shall consider several examples in which it has been possible to develop chemical methods for revealing the small difference in function between homozygous normal and heterozygous individuals. Additional examples can be found in recent reviews (Neel, 1953; Hsia, 1960).

Direct measurement of enzymes

A genetic defect in the production of an enzyme will result in a decrease in the enzyme from 0 to 50 percent, depending on the regulatory mechanisms involved. If the decrease is 0 percent, then there is little hope of demonstrating the presence of the gene. The production of antihemophilic globulin (AHG) is controlled by a gene on the X-chromosome. Males, with one X-chromosome, produce as much AHG as females, who have two. Females heterozygous for hemophilia, a disease in which AHG is not produced, usually have the normal amount of AHG. In this disease carriers cannot be recognized. This is probably true of many diseases inherited as sex-linked recessives, although, as more sensitive techniques are developed, more and more recessive diseases are found to be expressed in heterozygous individuals.

In a few diseases it is possible to obtain biological specimens, usually blood, that can be used to assay enzymes directly. The two diseases in which this has proved most successful are galactosemia and acatalasemia.

Acatalasemia. Catalase is an enzyme that decomposes hydrogen peroxide. It is found in many tissues of the body, including erythrocytes. In 1949 Takahara discovered patients with certain dental anomalies who appeared to lack catalase. Subsequent studies have confirmed the complete absence of catalase activity in these patients. The initial observations that the disease tends to occur in sibships has also been verified, and acatalasemia is now known to be inherited as a simple recessive trait. Although the disease has been sought in many localities, it has been reported only from Japan.

Neel (1959) has estimated that there are several hundred thousand carriers of the gene in Japan.

Measurements of erythrocyte catalase activity in proved heterozygotes (parents of affected individuals) reveal the interesting fact that heterozygotes produce only half as much enzyme as do normals. The values for the three classes are given in Fig. 6-1. Although there is variation within each class, the heterozygotes fall approximately

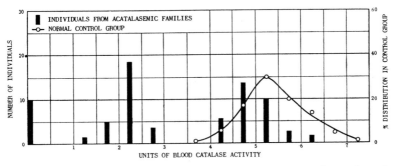

Fig. 6-1. Distribution of catalase values among members of acatalasemic families, compared to a curve based on a normal population. (From Nishimura, *et al.*, 1959.)

midway between the two homozygotes. This may be interpreted as indicating the independence of each gene in synthesizing its product. Alternatively, it must be assumed that the acatalasemia allele is producing a protein product that has lost its enzymic activity but is still capable of contributing to the product level so far as feedback regulatory mechanisms are concerned.

The utility of enzyme measurements in detecting heterozygotes is demonstrated in Fig. 6-2. In this pedigree the heterozygotes can be distinguished from homozygous normals.

Galactosemia. The nature of this disease has been discussed in previous chapters. The history of the efforts to detect carriers of the gene is interesting and informative. The first successful approach consisted in measuring the rapidity with which galactose can be metabolized in a *galactose tolerance test.* If a normal person ingests a large amount of galactose (40 grams), the blood level rises from the normal value of zero to about 25 mg per 100 ml. It then returns to normal within four hours, as shown in Fig. 6-3. Galactosemics,

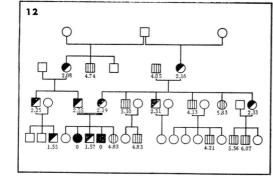

Fig. 6-2. A pedigree of acatalasemia. (From Nishimura, *et al.*, 1959.)

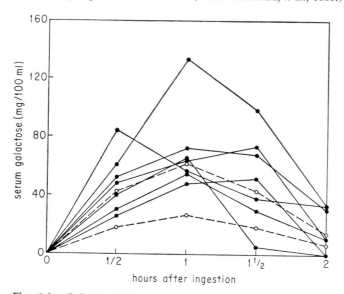

Fig. 6-3. Galactose tolerance curves for relatives of a galacto-semic patient. Forty grams of galactose was ingested at zero time. Solid lines: relatives of patient; lower dotted line: average control; upper dotted line: upper limit of normal. Most of the relatives shown are probably heterozygous for galactosemia. (Based on data from Holzel and Komrower, 1955.)

on the other hand, show an increase in plasma galactose that is strikingly greater than normal and persists for much longer times, since virtually the only mechanism for disposing of galactose in these patients is excretion into the urine. If the enzyme missing in galactosemia were deficient in heterozygotes, then the tolerance curve might rise above normal and might remain high for a longer time. As shown in Fig. 6-3, there is an abnormal response to galactose loading in heterozygotes. The difference from normal is very small, however. In fact, only about half the parents of galactosemics give abnormal curves, even though, on the assumption that galactosemia is a simple recessive trait, they would have to be heterozygotes (Holzel and Komrower, 1955). This observation led de Grouchy (1958) to suggest that some cases of galactosemia may result from heterozygosity at two different loci, only one of which produces the abnormal curve.

When it was recognized that the disease results from a lack of the enzyme galactose-1-phosphate uridyl transferase, it became possible to attempt better differentiation of heterozygotes by direct enzyme assays. Several groups have worked on this problem successfully (Hsia, et al., 1958; Kirkman and Bynum, 1959; Bretthauer, et al., 1959). Fig. 6-4 shows the results of an assay of erythrocyte enzyme levels. There is still some overlap of heterozygotes with normals, but most of the heterozygotes can be detected. On the basis of direct enzyme assays the trait is found to be inherited as a simple recessive.

Galactosemia illustrates the different degrees of discrimination that can be obtained with different methods. The best discrimination is obtained if the "primary" gene product, the enzyme, is measured directly by a good *in vitro* technique. It is not always possible to apply *in vitro* methods to an enzyme, however, and some information can be obtained by *in vivo* methods such as the tolerance test. In the case of galactosemia the tolerance test is not very good. It is much better in phenylketonuria.

Phenylketonuria. As outlined in a previous chapter, phenylketonuria results from a lack of phenylalanine hydroxylase activity. This enzyme is produced only by liver cells, and efforts to detect it in other cells or in body fluids have been fruitless. Heterozygotes could probably be identified from enzyme assays of small samples of liver, but the curiosity of normal individuals concerning their carrier status will not often lead to submission to a liver biopsy.

It is therefore necessary to consider procedures that are less interesting to the geneticist but more acceptable to the prospective heterozygote.

The tolerance test has proved quite useful in the case of phenylketonuria (Hsia, *et al.*, 1956). In the usual procedure, the subject ingests L-phenylalanine (0.1 g per kg body weight) and blood samples

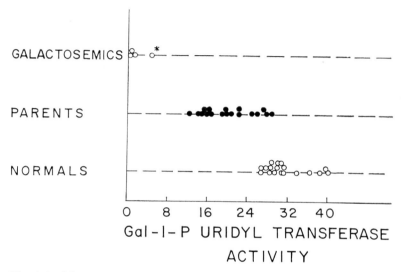

Fig. 6-4. Measurements of galactose-1-phosphate uridyl transferase in homozygous normal individuals and in individuals heterozygous and homozygous for galactosemia. The patient marked with an asterisk had received a transfusion. (From Kirkman and Bynum, 1959.)

are then taken at regular intervals. Heterozygotes metabolize this great excess of phenylalanine more slowly than do normals and the blood levels remain elevated for longer periods of time, as shown in Fig. 6-5. The greatest difference occurs about four hours after ingestion, and the blood levels at this time have been used to differentiate heterozygotes from normals. There is enough overlap between the two groups so that classification is often impossible, however.

Differences in blood levels of phenylalanine between heterozygotes and homozygous normals have been reported, even in the absence of a phenylalanine load. The distribution of plasma phenylalanine levels is shown in Fig. 6-6. About 20 percent of the population falls in the area of overlap of the two distributions where it is impossible to classify them accurately. By consideration of blood phenylalanine levels, both fasting and after a load, it is possible to assess the carrier status of all but a few percent of individuals.

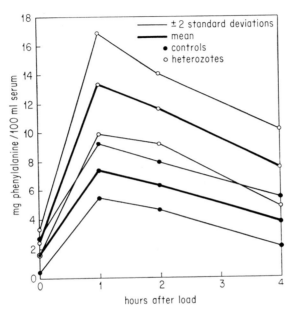

Fig. 6-5. Phenylalanine tolerance curves for normal individuals and for individuals heterozygous for phenylketonuria (parents of phenylketonurics). L-phenylalanine (0.1 g per kg body weight) is ingested at zero hours. (Based on data from Berry, Sutherland, and Guest, 1957.)

Measurement of nonenzymatic properties of protein

In a few instances it is possible to measure a protein product directly, as opposed to enzyme activity. The best known, of course, consists of the hemoglobinopathies. In this case very little could be gained by measuring enzyme activity—oxygen transporting ability. Since many of the mutations involve changes in physical properties of the hemoglobin molecules it is possible to recognize heterozygotes by the presence of the abnormal hemoglobin, usually from electro-

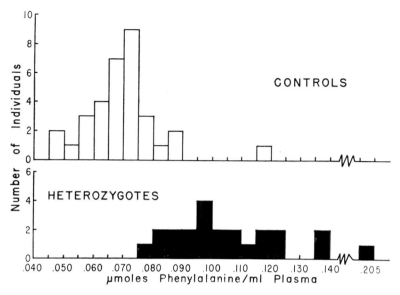

Fig. 6-6. Distributions of plasma phenylalanine levels in individuals who are heterozygous for phenylketonuria or who are homozygous normal. (From Knox and Messinger, 1958.)

phoretic studies. The hemoglobins have already been discussed in Chapter 3 and need not be further mentioned here.

The techniques that have proved so useful for hemoglobin may also be useful for other proteins and enzymes. The polymorphisms first reported by direct examination of proteins (haptoglobin, transferrin) have not yet been associated with disease states. The techniques have not been applied extensively to enzymes. On the basis of coding theory (Chapter 2) about half of the point mutations should result in an altered protein product, some of which would undoubtedly retain a degree of enzyme activity. It should therefore prove fruitful to look for altered enzymes, for example, by electrophoresis. One difficulty is that not all amino acid substitutions result in altered electrophoretic mobility. A further drawback is that enzymes are frequently restricted in their distribution within the body. Moreover, since the investigator nearly always has to rely on the specific enzyme activity of the altered protein for detection, he is necessarily limited to those mutations that, in the homozygous state, may not produce severe effects. The latter restriction may in part be overcome by the use of specific antibodies to detect proteins that have lost their enzymatic activity.

Potential means for detecting heterozygotes

At least two methods now in the early stages of development promise to be helpful in the recognition of genetic carriers. One of these is *in vitro* culture of human tissue. The technical difficulties that loomed so large only a few years ago have been greatly reduced. In many instances, however, new difficulties have arisen. Nevertheless, the principle has been established that human cells from a variety of tissues can be cultured for extended periods of time without apparent change in the constitution of the tissue and on media that are very nearly synthetic. The rate of progress in elucidating the fastidious nutritional requirements of differentiated cells and of working out conditions for isolating single viable cells gives hope that soon the problems of tissue culture will consist not of husbandry but of the intimate aspects of cell function.

Assuming that it will soon be possible to cultivate bits of tissue that can be separated from the donor without too much difficulty, it should be possible to establish the potential of the cells to produce either normal or less than normal amounts of a specific protein. It is also assumed that by that time the conditions for inducing production of any enzyme in any cell line will have been worked out. This is based on the theory that all cells have the information for producing all proteins in a given organism and will do so if repression can be avoided. This would enable the experimenter not only to measure the amount of enzyme activity but also to characterize the enzyme by physical and chemical studies. The superiority of *in vitro* studies of this type to *in vivo* studies is evident. With the rigid control over extracellular environment possible in tissue culture, most if not all of the overlap among genetic categories should be avoidable.

The previous techniques have been basically chemical studies. There is one technique that may be useful in recognizing the carrier state, whether it be a chemical trait or one not yet reduced to the chemical level. This is the study of linked markers. Genes closely associated on a chromosome are transmitted together, except when crossing over occurs between them. Since crossing over between any two markers is proportional to the distance between them, closely linked markers become dissociated infrequently. For example, the genes for the ABO antigens and for the nail-patella syndrome (a defect in the formation of fingernails and of patella) are located close to each other on the same chromosome (Renwick and Lawler, 1955).

Linkage as a means of identifying chromosomes is of no value at present because so little is known about linkage groups in man. Although many genes are recognized, most of them represent either rare dominants or recessives whose heterozygous expressions have not been identified. Consequently there has been little opportunity to study segregation of several of these genes in the same kindreds, a condition necessary to establish linkage relationships. A fruitful use of linkage will depend on loci for which at least two alleles occur with frequency. To what extent such loci exist is unknown, although, as laboratory techniques become refined, more and more genetic polymorphism is revealed. It is not too much to expect that enough loci will be established so that linkage groups will someday be a useful means of tracing individual chromosomes in human pedigrees. In many cases it will, of course, be simpler to follow a particular deleterious gene directly. In other cases it will undoubtedly be simpler to identify linked markers, by blood typing, electrophoresis of plasma, chromatography, etc. If there is a marker available on either side of the gene to be traced, then it can be identified with almost no error. It should be remembered that linkage is a means of following a particular chromosome in a particular pedigree. It will not be useful in population studies, since the association of alleles at different loci is random when the entire population is considered.

LITERATURE CITED

BERRY, H., SUTHERLAND, B., and GUEST, G. M., 1957. "Phenylalanine tolerance tests on relatives of phenylketonuric children," *Am. Jour. Human Genetics*, 9, 310–316.

BRETTHAUER, R. K., HANSEN, R. G., DONNELL, G., and BERGREN, W. R., 1959.

"A procedure for detecting carriers of galactosemia," *Proc Natl. Acad. Sci. U. S.*, **45**, 328–331.

Carson, P. E., Flanagan, C. L., Ickes, C. E., and Alving, A. S., 1956. "Enzymatic deficiency in primaquine-sensitive erythrocytes," *Science*, **124**, 484–485.

Childs, B., and Zinkham, W. H., 1959. "The genetics of primaquine sensitivity of the erythrocytes," in *Biochemistry of Human Genetics* (Ciba Foundation Symposium, Wolstenholme, G. E. W., and O'Connor, C. M., eds.), London: Churchill, pp. 76–89.

de Grouchy, J., 1958. *L'Hérédité Moléculaire. Conditions Normales et Pathologiques*, Rome: Istituto Gregorio Mendel.

Harris, H. W., Knight, R. A., and Selin, M. J., 1959. "Genetic factors influencing isoniazid blood levels in humans" [Abstract], *Am. Fed. for Clin. Res.* (January, 1959).

Holzel, A., and Komrower, G. M., 1955. "A study of the genetics of galactosaemia," *Arch. Dis. Childh.*, **30**, 155–159.

Hsia, D. Y.-Y., 1960. "Recent advances in biochemical detection of heterozygous carriers in hereditary diseases," *Metabolism*, **9**, 301–315.

———, Huang, I., and Driscoll, S. G., 1958. "The heterozygous carrier in galactosaemia," *Nature*, **182**, 1389–1390.

———, Driscoll, K. W., Troll, W., and Knox, W. E., 1956. "Detection by phenylalanine tolerance tests of heterozygous carriers of phenylketonuria," *Nature*, **178**, 1239–1240.

Kalow, W., 1959. "Cholinesterase types," in *Biochemistry of Human Genetics*, A Ciba Foundation Symposium (Wolstenholme, G. E. W., and O'Connor, C. M., eds.), London: Churchill, pp. 39–56.

Kirkman, H. N., and Bynum, E., 1959. "Enzymic evidence of a galactosemic trait in parents of galactosemic children," *Ann. Human Genetics*, **23**, 117–126.

Knox, W. E., and Messinger, E. C., 1958. "The detection in the heterozygote of the metabolic effect of the recessive gene for phenylketonuria," *Am. Jour. Human Genetics*, **10**, 53–60.

Neel, J. V., 1953. "The detection of the genetic carriers of inherited disease," in *Clinical Genetics* (Sorsby, A., ed.), London: Butterworth, pp. 27–34.

———, 1959. Discussion in *Biochemistry of Human Genetics*, A Ciba Foundation Symposium (Wolstenholme, G. E. W., and O'Connor, C. M., eds.), London: Churchill, pp. 131–132.

Nishimura, E. T., Hamilton, H. B., Kobara, T. Y., Takahara, S., Ogura, Y., and Doi, K., 1959. "Carrier state in human acatalasemia," *Science*, **130**, 333–334.

Reed, T. E., Chandler, J. H., Hughes, E. M., and Davidson, R. T., 1958. "Huntington's Chorea in Michigan. I. Demography and Genetics," *Am. Jour. Human Genetics*, **10**, 201–225.

Renwick, J. H., and Lawler, S. D., 1955. "Genetical linkage between the ABO and nail-patella loci," *Ann. Human Genetics*, **19**, 312–331.

Takahara, S., and Miyamoto, H., 1949. Cited in Nishimura, et al., 1959.

chapter seven

Treatment of
Inherited Diseases

A common misconception about inherited traits is that they cannot be treated. It is true that cures are usually impossible. It is also true, however, that, where the nature of the disease is understood, *control* is becoming increasingly possible. This is true of any disease, inherited or not. Even if the primary defect is unknown, the secondary effects responsible for the pathological process may be controllable. For example, diabetes mellitus has been largely controllable for many years; yet neither the primary block nor the precise genetic mechanism has been identified.

There is no point in attempting to classify all possible treatments for inherited diseases. The variations will be as numerous as the manifestations themselves. It may be instructive to consider some of the methods that have proved successful. These methods can be roughly classified into two categories—those designed to compensate for a deficiency of an essential metabolic product or hormone and those designed to prevent the deleterious effects of accumulated intermediates. These two approaches are not necessarily mutually exclusive, although examples are not known in which both have been applied.

COMPENSATION FOR A BIOCHEMICAL DEFICIENCY

Two types of deficiency may be considered on the basis of discussions in preceding chapters. The first is a deficiency of active protein that is due to a defective mechanism for its synthesis. This will result from mutation at one or at most two or three loci. Some examples are the protein hormones, enzymes, and the pigments involved in electron transport. The other type of deficiency involves small molecular weight metabolites and results from blocks in metabolism, either as a consequence of lack of some enzyme or inhibition of an enzyme.

The term "compensation" has been used advisedly in the heading for this section. Ideally one would like to supply the missing protein or metabolite. Practical considerations sometimes demand that one supply a substance farther along the metabolic pathway. In some cases it may be easier to influence the ultimate function of a pathway than to regulate the pathway itself. And there are instances, as in diabetes mellitus, where the primary defect is not known but where it is possible to restore metabolic balance by supplying a natural substance, such as insulin, or even unnatural substances, such as the sulfonylureas.

Hypothyroid cretinism

One of the better understood examples of artificial compensation for a series of metabolic blocks is hypothyroid cretinism. Cretinism results from a deficiency of thyroid hormone during early childhood. Although this in turn may result from a deficiency of dietary iodine, it is no longer a significant cause in the United States. Cretinism also occurs as a recessively inherited disease that cannot be prevented by supplying iodine in amounts adequate for thyroid function in normal people.

The chemical reactions involved in thyroid metabolism are show in Fig. 7-1. Six types of blocks that can lead to a deficiency of thyroid function have been recognized. (See Neel, *et al.,* 1960; Stanbury, 1960, for discussion and references.) The metabolic blocks involve such diverse reactions as the loss of ability to convert iodide to iodine and the loss of ability to remove iodine from mono- and diiodotyrosines. Since the pathological consequences of these blocks are due ultimately to deficiency of thyroid hormone, they can all be prevented by medication with thyroid extracts. It is essential to recognize the existence of a thyroid deficiency at a very early age; otherwise, serious irreversible effects on the nervous system will occur. This seems to be a common rule among diseases that are

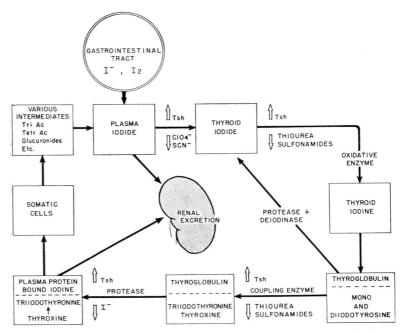

Fig. 7-1. The biochemical pathways of thyroid metabolism. (From Stanbury and McGirr, 1957.)

manifested during early childhood before the nervous system has matured.

Methemoglobinemia

Hemoglobin can function as an oxygen transport system only if the iron is maintained in the ferrous state. In normal people there is a slow, spontaneous oxidation of ferrous hemoglobin (reduced Hb) to give ferric hemoglobin (methemoglobin or MHb). A series of metabolic steps acts to maintain hemoglobin in the reduced form, beginning with the oxidation of carbohydrates and involving pyridine nucleotides and the enzyme or enzymes methemoglobin reductase. An equilibrium between the two forms of hemoglobin is thus set up.

$$Hb \rightleftharpoons MHb$$

Normally about 99 percent of the hemoglobin is in the reduced form. Two inherited conditions can occur that cause the proportion of MHb to increase greatly above normal. In one there is abnormal structure of the globin. This may then be considered as part of the abnormal hemoglobin series, involving structural changes that influence the redox equilibrium but not the electrophoretic mobility. Several such abnormal hemoglobins have been identified (Gerald, 1960; see also Fig. 3-6). This type of methemoglobinemia is expressed in the heterozygous condition.

In the other type of inherited methemoglobinemia, hemoglobin appears to be normal. In one family in which methemoglobinemia was inherited as a recessive, Gibson (1948) found a defect in the enzymes responsible for the reduction of MHb. The defective enzyme appeared to be a DPNH-dependent MHb reductase. It is of interest for this discussion to note that the enzymic defect can be by-passed in such patients by the administration of methylene blue. The mode of action is not certain, but it may involve activation of a separate enzyme that can react with MHb but that is distinguished from the usual reductase by its preferential reaction with TPNH and its requirement for a coenzyme such as methylene blue (Huennekens, et al., 1957). Ascorbic acid can also diminish the amount of MHb, but it is thought to do so by direct reaction with the MHb.

The recessive form of methemoglobinemia is an interesting example of a disease due to an enzyme deficiency in which therapy consists of providing an alternate mechanism for the enzyme activity. This approach to therapy has not been generally feasible.

Clotting disorders

Perhaps the most common examples of inherited protein deficiencies treated by replacement of the missing proteins are the clotting disorders. A number of diseases are now recognized in which there is a deficiency of an essential protein, either fibrinogen itself or one of the other proteins (for example, antihemophilic globulin) that function in the conversion of fibrinogen to fibrin. Most of the patients apparently lack the ability to synthesize the specific protein. The absence of any one of the proteins leads to inability of the blood to clot, giving rise therefore to uncontrolled bleeding.

The only effective means of restoring the ability to clot is by supplying the missing protein. This can be done either by injection of a specific blood fraction or by transfusion of whole blood. The effectiveness of these procedures lasts only as long as the injected protein remains in circulation. Since normally there is a constant turnover of blood proteins, the injected protein gradually disappears and, of course, cannot be replaced by the patient. Hence, effective maintenance of the ability to clot consists in renewing the missing factor frequently. The high rate at which the blood-clotting factors are removed from circulation precludes maintaining satisfactory levels except when required by a clinical emergency.

REMOVAL OF INHIBITORS

In many diseases the pathological defects arise from the accumulation of blocked intermediates. Therapy consists in disposing of the intermediates or in preventing their formation in excessive quantities.

Phenylketonuria

This interesting disease is the most recent to yield to efforts at regulation. The nature of the metabolic block was reviewed on p. 79. The inability to convert phenylalanine to tyrosine does not result in a deficiency of tyrosine, which is found in the diet in more than adequate quantities. Therefore, the deleterious effects of this gene are due to the accumulation of the substrate phenylalanine. The treatment accordingly must be designed to prevent accumulation of phenylalanine or toxic by-products. It might also be possible to prevent the deleterious effects in the various tissues where they occur. Too little is known about these effects to devise a logical attack on the problem.

In a previous chapter evidence was presented that the pathological effects of phenylketonuria are due to secondary blocks. These, in turn, result from inhibition of enzymes, including amino acid decarboxylases, by one or more of the compounds that form with increased levels of phenylalanine. A successful treatment might therefore consist in removal of phenylalanine from the diet of affected individuals. Phenylalanine is normally consumed as a constituent of protein. Unfortunately, there are no known proteins that are low in content of phenylalanine. Nearly all proteins contain approximately 6 percent phenylalanine. In order to remove the phenylalanine it is necessary to hydrolyze the protein (usually casein), pass the hydrolyzate through charcoal to remove aromatic amino acids, and then restore the levels of aromatic amino acids other than phenylalanine to proper nutritional levels.

This procedure is expensive, and it has been only in the last few years that it has become feasible. The first attempts at placing phenylketonurics on this diet were reported in 1954 (Bickel, et al.). The early attempts did little to improve mental ability. It was noted, however, that usually hyperactive patients became much more manageable on low phenylalanine diets. It soon became apparent that the age of the patient is of prime importance for a successful response. If a low phenylalanine diet is started within the first few months of life, the patient may escape the major defects associated with phenylketonuria. If treatment is delayed beyond that point, the degree of success becomes proportionately smaller. The point beyond which therapy is of no value is not established. Some investigators believe that no benefit occurs after the patient has reached two to three years of age. Others think that some benefit is derived several years beyond that. Delayed treatment might result in an I.Q. of 40, say, as against an I.Q. of 25 with no treatment. Not everyone agrees that such a difference justifies the considerable expense and effort of controlling the diet.

The effectiveness of dietary control on aromatic compounds is shown in Fig. 7-2. Within a few days after the diet is instituted blood phenylalanine drops from 25 to 50 mg per 100 ml to within the normal range of 1 to 2 mg per 100 ml. In some cases studied experimentally the diet was completely lacking in phenylalanine during the initial stages of treatment. Once the blood phenylalanine reached normal levels, phenylalanine was restored to the diet in amounts that would maintain the blood level in the proper range. Patients need some phenylalanine, since they must build proteins with it even though they are unable to metabolize the excess. The necessity of maintaining a given level requires that those on the diet be observed carefully. If too little phenylalanine is given the patient not only fails to synthesize essential proteins but also breaks down body proteins already formed and goes into negative nitrogen balance. Successful treatment then consists in striking a delicate balance between malnutrition and intoxication. The increase in intelligence in a successfully treated patient is accompanied by increased ingenuity in supplementing surreptitiously his rather unpalatable diet, thus making the job of regulation still more difficult.

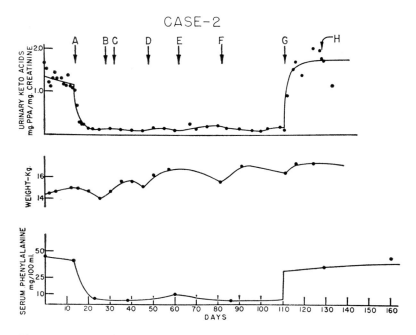

Fig. 7-2. The effect of restricted phenylalanine intake on the levels of blood phenylalanine and urinary keto acids (expressed as phenylpyruvic acid) in a four-year-old phenylketonuric patient. A, low phenylalanine diet started; G, normal diet resumed. (From Armstrong and Tyler, 1955.)

If treatment of phenylketonurics is to be started at the most propitious time, the condition must be detected within the first few weeks of life. The number of individuals who have been detected at this age is still very small. The primary reason is that phenylketonuria is so rare. The birth frequency of phenylketonurics is approximately 1 per 25,000. This would correspond to a gene frequency of $\frac{1}{160}$; since each person has two chromosomes, the frequency of phenylketonuria carriers is $\frac{1}{80}$. The frequency of marriages between carriers would be $\frac{1}{80} \times \frac{1}{80} = \frac{1}{6400}$. Phenylketonuria is a recessive trait. The frequency among the offspring of such marriages would therefore be $\frac{1}{4}$. Hence the probability of a child's being phenylketonuric is $\frac{1}{4} \times \frac{1}{6400} \cong \frac{1}{25,000}$. If a program for testing all newborns were set up the returns would be extremely small in terms of numbers of patients detected per number of individuals tested. Yet, with a birth rate of 4.5 million per year in the United States, there are 180 phenylketonurics born here each year.

A complicating factor in detecting phenylketonurics among newborns is the delayed appearance of the trait most easily tested—the excretion of phenylpyruvic acid in urine. It is not excreted until the blood level of phenylalanine is quite elevated. Although some infants reach this state within a few days, others may not do so for five or six weeks. It is to be hoped that an effective testing program can be designed. Once a phenylketonuric has been detected it is imperative that any subsequent child born into that sibship be tested until he is past the age at which the chemical effects may initially appear. Such siblings have one chance in four of being affected. This can be contrasted with the one chance in 25,000 among the general population. It is among the siblings of known phenylketonurics that cases have been found at only a few weeks of age.

If the central nervous system is particularly sensitive to the effects of toxic substances in the neonatal period, might it then be more resistant in an older child? If it is, it might be possible to discontinue treatment once the patient has passed the sensitive period. A satisfactory answer has not been obtained, chiefly because the dietary treatment has not been available long enough for those children detected in the neonatal period. It appears that children carried on the diet for several years are not subject to the severe effects of the toxic substances. It is not obvious yet that they escape all further effects.

Galactosemia

Galactosemia, like phenylketonuria, results in the accumulation of a toxic product, galactose-1-phosphate. It should be possible to prevent the accumulation of galactose-1-phosphate by restricting the galactose intake, as it is with phenylketonuria. The only common source of galactose is in the form of lactose in milk, and it is a relatively simple matter to eliminate milk from the diet. Children with galactosemia respond dramatically on a milk-free diet (Komrower, *et al.*, 1956). The aminoaciduria, a prominent feature of the disease, disappears almost immediately. Other changes may not be so readily reversible. If the central nervous system has been affected the child will remain defective in spite of treatment, but without treatment the results are much worse, usually involving severe mental defect or death.

Unlike phenylketonuria, galactosemia involves metabolites that are not essential for normal metabolism. Consequently there is no need to regulate the galactose level at other than zero. This greatly simplifies the matter of dietary control. Furthermore, the product of the blocked enzyme, uridinediphosphogalactose (UDPGal), can be synthesized in a galactosemic patient by reversal of the epimerase step. By this means it is possible for an affected person to synthesize the galactose required for certain brain lipids which contain galactose. UDPGal would seem to be the intermediate for incorporation of galactose into essential body constituents.

PROSPECTS FOR TREATMENT OF INHERITED DISEASES

Therapeutic methods that have not been developed cannot be systematized. It is nevertheless interesting to speculate on potential means of controlling metabolic derangements. In addition to the methods described in the previous discussion, there are several theoretical methods that have not yet been applied.

One possible method would be to prevent formation of inhibiting intermediates that accumulate because of a metabolic block. In the reaction sequence

$$A \xrightarrow{E_1} B \overset{E_2}{\dashrightarrow} C$$

compound B or some related substance B_1 will frequently accumulate, thereby interfering with other enzyme reactions. Let us assume that compound A is less toxic, either because other pathways are available that prevent its accumulation or because it is less active as an inhibitor. If the conversion of A to B could be blocked, then the deleterious effects of the block at E_2 could be avoided. For purposes of discussion we will assume that compound C is nonessential or can be supplied externally.

There are at least two ways in which enzyme E_1 might be blocked —by inhibition of its activity, and by suppression of its synthesis. The former would make use of inhibitors that specifically block the activity of the enzyme. Such inhibitors might be chemical analogs of compound A that complex with E_1 but cannot undergo reaction. Competitive inhibitors of this type would have to interfere predominantly with E_1 and not with other enzymes acting on A. It is not essential that the inhibition be competitive, but there is little basis at present for designing other inhibitors with the required specificity.

An instance where such an inhibitor might be useful is found in phenylketonuria. If the conversion of phenylalanine to phenylpyruvic acid were blocked, then most of the deleterious effects observed in this disease might be avoided. It would be necessary to dispose of the even larger amounts of phenylalanine that would accumulate, although perhaps the renal threshold for phenylalanine would prevent the build-up of much higher blood levels than occur anyway. Similarly, in galactosemia, the accumulated galactose per se is probably benign. If an inhibitor of galactokinase were available that did not also inhibit the phosphorylation of glucose, then the disease might be treated by administration of the inhibitor to the patient.

The second way of blocking the activity of E_1, by suppressing its synthesis, is commonly achieved by increasing the level of some product of a metabolic pathway. Thus, in the reaction sequence given above, the synthesis of both E_1 and E_2 might be influenced by the amount of C present. If it were possible artificially to raise the level of C, then the amount of B produced might be correspondingly decreased.

A possible example of this approach is found in oroticaciduria (Huguley, et al., 1959). The one patient recognized with this disease excreted about 1.5 grams of orotic acid per day on a normal diet. Conventional therapeutic approaches proved ineffective in correcting the megaloblastic anemia of the patient or the excretion of orotic acid. Orotic acid is an intermediate on the biosynthetic pathway of pyrimidines, and Yates and Pardee (1956) showed that in E. coli the formation of ureidosuccinic acid, the first intermediate specifically on the pathway to pyrimidines, is inhibited by pyrimidine end products. On the assumption that an analogous pathway might exist in man, the oroticaciduria patient was given a yeast extract rich in uridylic and cytidylic acids. These nucleotides proved most effective in reducing the excretion of their precursor, orotic acid, and in correcting other pathological features of the disease. The patient probably had an enzyme block at a step following orotic acid synthesis, but the exact position of the block was not established. It is to be expected that, as our knowledge of the nature of enzyme repression grows, application to other disease states will become possible.

One possibility for treatment that may become feasible is the transplantation of normal tissue into a diseased patient. Where the block in metabolism involves compounds of intermediary metabolism that can diffuse in and out of cells, it should be possible to regulate the levels throughout the entire body by the presence of some normal tissue. The greatest success would be expected with liver transplants, since the liver is the organ responsible for many of the reactions of intermediary metabolism.

The principal difficulty with tissue transplantation techniques arises from the ability of the recipient to reject any tissue that is antigenically different from his own. For this reason, successful organ transplants or skin grafts are obtained only between identical twins. Work with small mammals has given hope that this obstacle can be overcome. In the most promising procedure the foreign tissue is introduced during the neonatal period when the ability of the recipient to form antibodies is minimal. Under these circumstances the recipient manages to work out a *modus vivendi* so that it is compatible with the foreign tissue, even at later stages of the life cycle. Another method of inducing compatibility is to irradiate an animal heavily before introducing the transplant. This temporarily destroys the ability to make antibodies, recreating a situation superficially parallel to the neonatal period. Both of these techniques for inducing histocompatibility have proved successful in laboratory animals but they have not been used with unequivocal success in man. This is partly because the techniques are new and opportunities to explore them inadequate. There is every reason to suppose that with appropriate modification they will prove useful in man and provide thereby a means of overcoming some blocks in metabolism. An interesting review of the problem of immunological tolerance was given by Medawar in his Nobel address (Medawar, 1961).

Projecting considerably into the future, Pauling (1956) has suggested that artificial enzymes may one day be used to correct inherited deficiencies. It should be possible, once the intimate details of mechanism of a given enzyme-catalyzed reaction are known, to synthesize a catalyst that can function in the same manner as the enzyme. Such a catalyst might not have the same efficiency as the enzyme—indeed, it might be more efficient. It also might be less specific in its action on substrates. Nevertheless, it could prevent the accumulation of large amounts of some blocked intermediate. The catalyst would probably be imbedded on a solid matrix, which in turn would be contained in a tube (perhaps of polyethylene) inserted into a vein so that blood would continuously flow through it. That such an idea is not too fanciful is indicated by the work of Wang (1955), who reproduced the active site of the catalase molecule with triethylenetetramine plus iron and obtained a very potent catalase.

There is another potential procedure for treatment of inherited diseases, equally speculative. It consists in the directed alteration of defective genes to functional genes. The most likely method would be an extension of genetic transformation as observed in bacteria (Chapter 2). DNA from a normal individual would be introduced into the diseased person, where it would be able to replicate and produce functional ribosomes. The introduction might involve either an extract of DNA or a virus carrier, as in bacterial transduction. In order for the introduced DNA to function it would have to enter at least some of the host cells so that it could associate with the host DNA, perhaps recombining with the chromosomes of the host to give new arrays of genes. A recent report suggests that it is possible for DNA to enter cells in tissue culture (Gartler, 1959). It is difficult at present to determine whether or not this approach will ever become feasible. A number of studies that have direct bearing on questions raised here are being carried out. The approach cannot be dismissed until much more is known of the limits on the manipulation of DNA.

In the final section of this chapter an attempt has been made to enumerate some of the means of correcting metabolic disease that can be anticipated at this time. It is the history of science that most of the ideas of this type ultimately fall short of their objective but that new ideas are developed that frequently achieve more than originally hoped for. On this basis we may anticipate new developments that will solve much better some of the problems of control of metabolic errors.

LITERATURE CITED

ARMSTRONG, M. D., and TYLER, F. H., 1955. "Studies on phenylketonuria. I. Restricted phenylalanine intake in phenylketonuria," *Jour. Clin. Invest.*, **34**, 565–580.

BICKEL, H., GERRARD, J., and HICKMANS, E. M., 1954. "The influence of phenylalanine intake on the chemistry and behaviour of a phenylketonuric child," *Acta Paediat.*, **43**, 64.

GARTLER, S. M., 1959. "Cellular uptake of deoxyribonucleic acid by human tissue culture cells," *Nature*, **184**, 1505–1506.

GERALD, PARK S., 1960. "The hereditary methemoglobinemias," in *The Metabolic Basis of Inherited Diseases* (Stanbury, J. B., Wyngaarden, J. B., and Frederickson, D., eds.), New York: McGraw-Hill, pp. 1068–1085.

GIBSON, Q. H., 1948. "The reduction of methaemoglobin in red blood cells and studies on the cause of idiopathic methaemoglobinaemia," *Biochem. Jour.*, **42**, 13–23.

HUENNEKENS, F. M., CAFFREY, R. W., BASFORD, R. E., and GABRIO, B. W., 1957. "Erythrocyte metabolism. IV. Isolation and properties of methemoglobin reductase," *Jour. Biol. Chem.*, **227**, 261–272.

HUGULEY, C. M., JR., BAIN, J. A., RIVERS, S. L., and SCOGGINS, R. B., 1959. "Refractory megaloblastic anemia associated with excretion of orotic acid," *Blood*, **14**, 615–634.

KOMROWER, G. M., SCHWARZ, V., HOLZEL, A., and GOLBERG, L., 1956. "A clinical and biochemical study of galactosaemia," *Arch. Dis. Childh.*, **31**, 254–264.

MEDAWAR, P. B., 1961. "Immunological tolerance," *Science*, **133**, 303–306.

NEEL, J. V., CARR, E. A., JR., BEIERWALTES, W. H., and DAVIDSON, R. T., 1961. "Genetic studies on the congenitally hypothyroid," *Pediatrics*, **27**, 269–285.

PAULING, L., 1956. "The future of enzyme research," in *Enzymes: Units of Biological Structure and Function* (Gaebler, O. H., ed.), New York: Academic Press, pp. 177–182.

STANBURY, J. B., 1960. "Familial goiter," in *The Metabolic Basis of Inherited Diseases* (Stanbury, J. B., Wyngaarden, J. B., and Frederickson, D., eds.), New York: McGraw-Hill, pp. 273–320.

————, and McGIRR, E. M., 1957. "Sporadic or non-endemic familial cretinism with goiter," *Am. Jour. Med.*, **22**, 712.

WANG, J. H., 1955. "Detailed mechanism of a new type of catalase-like action," *Jour. Am. Chem. Soc.*, **77**, 4715–4719.

YATES, R. A., and PARDEE, A. B., 1956. "Control of pyrimidine biosynthesis in *Escherichia coli* by a feed-back mechanism," *Jour. Biol. Chem.*, **221**, 757–770.

index